cLv

Werner Gitt

Stars and their Purpose

Signposts in Space

clv

Christliche
Literatur-Verbreitung e.V.
Postfach 11 01 35 · 33661 Bielefeld

The Author, Prof. Dr-Ing. Werner Gitt was born in Raineck/East Prussia in 1937. In 1963 he enrolled at the Technical University of Hanover (Technische Hochschule Hannover) and in 1968 he completed his studies as Diplom Ingenieur. Thereafter he worked as an assistant at the Institute of Control Engineering at the Technical University of Aachen (Technische Hochschule Aachen). Following two years of research work, he received his doctorate summa cum laude, together with the prestigious Borchers Medal, from the Technical University of Aachen, Germany, in 1970. He is now Director and Professor at the German Federal Institute of Physics (Physikalisch-Technische Bundesanstalt Braunschweig). He has written numerous scientific papers in the field of information science, numerical mathematics, and control engineering, as well as several popular books, some of which have been translated into Bulgarian, Czech, English, Finnish, French, Hungarian, Italian, Croatian, Kirghizian, Polish, Rumanian and Russian. Since 1984 he has been a regular guest lecturer at the State Independent Theological University of Basle, Switzerland on the subject of 'The Bible and Science'. He has held lectures on related topics at numerous universities at home and abroad, as well as having spoken on the topic Faith and Science in a number of different countries (e.g. Austria, Belgium, Hungary, Kazakhstan, Kirghizia, Lithuania, Namibia, Norway, Rumania, Russia, South Africa, Sweden, Switzerland).

1st English edition 1996
2nd English edition 2000

© of the German edition:
Werner Gitt, "Signale aus dem All – Wozu gibt es Sterne?"
1993 by CLV · Christliche Literatur-Verbreitung e.V.
Postfach 11 01 35 · D-33661 Bielefeld (Germany)

© of the English edition:
1996 by CLV · Christliche Literatur-Verbreitung e.V.
Postfach 11 01 35 · D-33661 Bielefeld (Germany)

Translation to English: Prof. Dr Jaap Kies
Correction: Mrs Marianne Rothe, Russell Grigg,
          Dr Carl Wieland
Cover: Dieter Otten, Bergneustadt
Typography: CLV
Printed in Germany: by Ebner Ulm

ISBN 3-89397-787-2

Index

Preface

Astronomy is one of the oldest sciences. The stars were studied systematically in the ancient civilisations of Babylon, Egypt, China, and Central America as early as the third millennium before Christ. Such observations were used for measuring time and for constructing calendars. Those astronomers were able to predict eclipses of the sun and of the moon, as well as the positions of the planets. During the sixth and fifth centuries before Christ the Greeks continued building on the achievements of the Babylonian astronomers. Important milestones in the history of astronomy include the theory of heliocentricity (which superseded the Ptolemaic view), the discovery of *Kepler's* laws, and the mathematical formulation of celestial mechanics. By means of these laws various calculations and predictions could be made about the planets, their satellites, and the comets. Astrophysics became a science in the nineteenth century, and in the twentieth century radio astronomy was developed, as well as infrared, X-ray and gamma-ray astronomy. Early ventures into space culminated in the first moon landing on 20 July 1969. Astronomical facts have a special fascination for scientists as well as laymen.

The problems of astronomy: As a science, astronomy attempts to explain the immeasurable aspects of space in measurable terms – a nearly impossible task. Physical laws which are valid on earth, are applied to the entire universe. Thus astronomy becomes applied physics on the largest scale imaginable. Matter occurring in space is no different from that of which the earth is made, but it is subject to conditions unobtainable on earth. Pressure and density can be so extreme as to be totally unknown on earth. Matter (atoms and electrons) can be so tightly packed that the total mass of the earth could be compressed into a thimble. On the other hand, space can be so empty that a cubic meter contains only one atom of hydrogen.

The limitations of astronomy: Every science has its limitations and boundaries which cannot be crossed, no matter how hard we try. In the words of one astronomer: "The only available tangibles are a few exposed photographic plates, recordings of radio signals from space and from space probes, some rocks from the moon, and meteorites which have fallen from the sky." *Harold Urey*, who won a Nobel prize for chemistry, brashly declared that he would explain the origin of the universe by studying one moon rock. Moon rocks have become available, but no answers are forthcoming. Although some old questions have been answered, even more new problems have arisen.

God teaches us something about our limitations through his prophet Isaiah:

> "For my thoughts are not your thoughts, neither are your ways my ways, declares the LORD. As the heavens are higher than the earth, so are my ways higher than your ways and my thoughts than your thoughts" (Isaiah 55: 8,9).

God reveals His thoughts in two ways: In the Bible, and in His creation. In spite of intensive research no biologist, chemist or engineer has as yet been able to understand fully the brilliantly devised process of photosynthesis, not to mention the (im)possibility of imitating it. But the Creator has installed this wonderful ability in even the smallest blade of grass. We encounter fascinating frontiers in all kinds of scientific endeavour here on earth. It is no surprise then, that we are greatly challenged when it comes to investigating the universe. We do not know its structure nor its spatial relationships. Where are its boundaries if it is finite? Is the universe an open system or is it closed?

Can the vast distances be accounted for if the universe is "young"? According to the evolutionary view, the light of a star which is millions of light-years distant, must have taken millions of years to reach us. This places a minimum on the age of the universe. All too often vague theories, conjectures, or even plain speculations parade as certain knowledge. *Steven Weinberg*, who was awarded the Nobel prize for physics in 1979, honestly concedes that he gets a feeling of unreality when he writes as if he really knew what it was about [W2, p 18]. The well-known German astronomer, *Otto Heckmann*, says that a dense cloud hides the conditions prevailing when the cosmos was formed and those prevailing at its boundaries. Boundary conditions are observed on a backwards-extending light cone that covers a finite range only. Observational data become progressively less accurate and eventually meaningless as distances increase, because of the limitations of our instruments [H2, p 134]. *Edwin Hubble* (1889 – 1953) also emphasised the limits and uncertainty which characterise astronomical findings [L3, p 181]:

> Our deep space investigations end with a question mark. How could it be otherwise? We have some knowledge of our immediate neighbours, but our knowledge diminishes very rapidly as the distance increases. Eventually we reach the last frontier at the observational limits of our telescopes where only vague glimmers can be perceived. There we measure mere shadows, and amidst ghostly errors of spectral measurement we look for milestones which are hardly more real than ghosts or spectres.

Theme of this book: Many fascinating facts about the stars, the galaxies and the planets have become known by means of present-day observational techniques. There are, however, astronomical questions that will never be resolved in spite of all our efforts, because the greatness of the LORD Who created everything, cannot be fathomed (Ps 145:3). Even his works are unfathomable. His works which are studied in astronomy, are much less fathomable than those involving other sciences. For some questions, however, we do have answers as given in the Bible: Why do all the stars and the immense universe exist? Who created them? Whose ideas and purposes are implemented? Are we dealing with chance and necessity, or with a brilliant master plan? Is it possible to know the Creator personally? Answers to such questions are not found in astronomy books and journals, but it is exactly these questions that will be discussed in this book, because such questions concern us personally and answers may be found in the Bible, as we shall see.

Aids to understanding: Although not an astronomy textbook, this book includes many new discoveries of this quickly expanding science. Explanatory footnotes are provided when new concepts are mentioned for the first time. Other important terms are discussed more fully in the Appendix (Chapter A3). Such terms are indicated with an arrow (e.g. → celestial sphere). Most Bible references are quoted directly, to avoid having to look them up. Except where indicated, the *New International Version* has been used. References to apocryphal books have been taken from *The Jerusalem Bible*, London, Darton, Longman & Todd, 1966 edition. When reference is made to the apocryphal 'Ecclesiasticus' (not to be confused with 'Ecclesiastes'), 'Sira', the name of the author (abbreviation: Sir) is used to avoid confusion.

Readership and purpose of this book: No specific educational level or age group has been targeted. Those works of creation studied in astronomy are so fascinating that everybody should be interested, regardless of profession or standing. Astronomical facts are correlated with biblical pronouncements. Very few books, if any, cover this aspect, and it is the sincere desire of the author that believers will acknowledge the greatness of God when contemplating the vastness of the universe and its stars. Wonder may then become worship. Another important purpose is that the seeking or doubting person should find God and obtain assurance of salvation.

A note of thanks: The manuscript was scrutinised by Dr *Norbert Pailer* (Meersburg, Germany), *Andreas Wolff* (Giessen, Germany), and the publishers, CLV, after indepth discussions with my wife. I am grateful for all their suggestions and additions.

Werner Gitt

Preface to the English Edition

As author I am delighted that my book is now available in English. Prof. *Jaap Kies* (Cape Town, South Africa) was responsible for the arduous task of translating the book into his mother tongue. Mrs *Marianne Rothe* (Johannesburg, South Africa) and Dr *Carl Wieland* together with *Russell Grigg* (Australia) proof read the translation thoroughly. I would like to thank all of those involved for their work in bringing this book into being. May it be a help to those who are seeking and asking questions as well as to those who already believe.

Werner Gitt

1. Introduction

All of us must occasionally have wondered why there are stars in the sky. This book deals with this very question. Arguments and answers are based on numerous astronomical facts, as well as on the Bible. To my mind scientific findings and biblical affirmations are inseparable. It is a tragic fact of history that these two approaches have diverged and have become separated.

The well-known Psalm 19 provides a first answer:

1. The heavens declare the glory of God; the skies proclaim the work of his hands.
2. Day after day they pour forth speech; night after night they display knowledge.
3. There is no speech or language where their voice is not heard.
4. Their voice goes out into all the earth, their words to the ends of the world. In the heavens He has pitched a tent for the sun,
5. which is like a bridegroom coming forth from his pavilion, like a champion rejoicing to run his course.
6. It rises at one end of the heavens and makes its circuit to the other; nothing is hidden from its heat.

The Hebrew word for heavens (v. 1) is *shamayim*, which has more than one meaning, as in English and in other languages. It can mean the earth's atmosphere (Gen 1:20), or the starry heavens (Gen 1:15), or the place where God dwells (Ps 14:2). In every case the context determines the meaning[1]; it is clear that Psalm 19 refers to the stars. This

---

1 **Polysemy** (Greek *polos* = many; *sema* = sign, *semantikos* = having significance): Linguistically polysemy indicates ambiguity of a word. The context indicates the appropriate meaning.

is a good place to start developing our subject. Various interesting and related topics are discussed in the following chapters, culminating in the last chapter where the purpose of this book is revealed and the questions are resolved. We will now respond to Jeremiah 51 verse 10: "Come, let us tell … what the LORD our God has done."

2. Can the Stars be Counted?

People have always been fascinated by the stars and many have tried to count them. When God promised Abraham that he would have innumerable descendants, He drew a striking comparison: "Look up at the heavens and count the stars – if indeed you can count them." Then He said to him, "So shall your offspring be" (Gen 15:5). Stars up to the sixth → magnitude[2] are visible to the naked eye. The total number of individual stars visible in both the northern and the southern → celestial hemispheres is about 6,000. On a clear night one can thus see at most 3,000 stars at the same time. Is that it? With the advent of telescopes very many previously unknown stars were discovered. *Galileo* (1564 – 1642) was probably the first person to do that, using his home-made telescope. In his famous work, *Sidereus nuncius* (1610), he wrote:

> "It is really astounding to be able to add an innumerable number of fixed stars to the large number which we have been aware of up to now. These others which have never before been seen, have now become visible and comprise a tenfold increase in the number of stars."

Galileo saw a tenfold increase in the number of visible stars, i. e. up to 30,000. From 1852 to 1859 *F. W. Argelander* completed his survey and counted 324,198 stars up to the

---

2 **Star magnitudes:** The apparent brightness of stars as seen from earth. The scale of magnitudes does not reflect the actual sizes of the stars. The Greek astronomer, *Hipparchus* (about 190 BC to 125 BC), divided the visible stars into six brightness groups, the first magnitude being the brightest, and the sixth those which are barely visible. With the advent of telescopes, the scale was extended. This is discussed more fully in Appendix A3 (p.205-206) (key word: "Star magnitude").

9th magnitude. The number of stars was once more increased by a factor of ten.

The largest earth-bound telescopes using photographic plates and long exposure times, have made three thousand million stars visible in each hemisphere (= celestial hemisphere), most of which belong to the local Milky Way galaxy. Each half of the → celestial sphere comprises an area equal to 100,000 full moons as seen from earth. It follows that about 30,000 stars occupy an area equal to the full moon. The total number of stars which *Galileo* could see, can today be observed in an area no larger than the apparent size of moon! Is this the upper limit?

The local Milky Way galaxy has been found to contain 200 thousand million stars – what an astounding result! If somebody could count three stars per second, then, after 100 years, he would have counted only five percent of this number. Our galaxy comprises not only an unimaginable host of stars, but the size of this bright starry band in the sky is also astounding. Its diameter is said to be 100,000 light-years. Astronomical distances are too large to be measured in kilometres, so light-years are used instead. One light-year is the distance that a light ray travels in one year. At a speed of 300,000 km per second, it amounts to 9.46 million million kilometres. The total mass of all the stars in the Milky Way amounts to 200 thousand million times the mass of the sun, which is 2×10^{27} tonnes, or 333,000 times the mass of the earth. Can we really grasp these large masses and those immense sizes and distances?

And is this the only galaxy? No, with the naked eye we can see three more, namely the two Clouds of Magellan near the southern celestial pole, and the Andromeda galaxy in the constellation of the same name (designated M31 in *Messier's* catalogue[3], or NGC 224 in the *New Gen-*

---

3 **Star catalogue:** The first printed catalogues of nebulae were published in the middle of the 18th century. These were systematically organised lists of star

eral Catalogue of Nebulae and Clusters of Stars). Andromeda was recognised as a galaxy consisting of individual stars as late as 1923, by means of the 2.5 m mirror telescope at Mt. Wilson. This galaxy is thought to be 2.25 million light-years from us[4]. Its total light emission is equal to 2,500 million times that of the sun. However, at this distance stars having the same luminosity as the sun can no longer be proved to exist by the use of optical telescopes. The Andromeda galaxy is the most distant object in the universe that can be seen by the naked eye, except for the occasional supernova.

Numerous other galaxies were discovered by means of the prolonged exposure of photographic plates. According to currently available data there are 100 million gala-

---

groupings like the Milky Way, and also gaseous nebulae like the one in Orion. In 1755 *N. de la Caille* published a list of 42 nebulae, and *C. Messier's* (1730 – 1817) catalogue of 103 objects appeared in 1780 and 1781. It is still known under his name. Later another astronomer, *F. W. Herschel* (1738 – 1822), compiled a list of 2,500 nebulae. The *New General Catalogue of Nebulae and Clusters of Stars* (NGC) appeared in 1888, compiled by the Danish astronomer *J. Dreyer* (1852 – 1926). During the period 1990 to 1992 the first catalogue of X-ray stars (with 60,000 stars) was compiled by the German X-ray satellite, ROSAT.

4 **Astronomical distances:** Radar and laser techniques can be employed for measuring the distances in the solar system. Greater distances require the use of parallax, the apparent displacement of an object against the distant background when the observer moves in a direction perpendicular to the line of sight. The distance of certain stars, known as cepheid variables, can be estimated by their period of variability and their apparent brightness. For distances greater than ten million light-years estimates are based on the red-shift phenomenon. It should be noted that the measurement of very large distances in particular are subject to great uncertainty, both because of the limited accuracy of the measurements, and the supposed meaning of the red shift. One should be very careful with the red shift. The displacement found in star spectra is not interpreted according to the Doppler effect but according to the expansion of the universe, so that the calculated distances depend strongly on the cosmological model ("big bang") and on the value of the Hubble constant. As a result of this uncertainty only the measured value, z, of the red shift (the displacement factor) is often given, and not the estimated distance, which depends on calculations based on the preferred model. Because no other data is available, this book employs the published distances, with the reservation that they are not really dependable.

xies with stellar magnitudes of up to 21. The actual number could be appreciably larger, because only galaxies up to apparent magnitude 23 lying within a distance of a few thousand million light-years, can be observed. Furthermore, small galaxies are difficult to detect. Probably the world's best telescope is that of the European Organisation for Astronomical Research, (ESO) located in Chili. The faintest galaxies that can be detected on a photographic plate, appear 1,600 million times less bright than stars that can just be seen by the naked eye. A glowing cigar on the moon will have the same apparent brightness on earth as the faintest observable galaxy. Attempts to count even the farthest and the faintest galaxies, are continuing. To this end charge coupled devices (CCD's) are directed at a particular spot in the sky for up to six hours. This process is repeated with different filters to obtain information about the colours of the light emitted by the galaxies. *J. A. Tyson* of the Bell Laboratories and *P. Seitzer* of the National Optical Observatories have succeeded in detecting galaxies up to stellar magnitude 27, covering between 70 and 80 percent of the area of the celestial sphere.

The total number of galaxies discovered thus far, is probably in the region of several hundred thousand million, and it may even amount to a few million million.

One of the most startling astronomical discoveries is that galaxies occur in clusters, which can be extremely large. The average diameter of such a cluster is about three million light-years. The best-known cluster, consisting of 2,500 galaxies, is Virgo, at an average distance of 70 million light-years from earth. Its diameter is 130,000 light-years, and *E. Holmberg* estimates that its total mass is equal to 790 thousand million suns. In contrast to Virgo, the Hercules cluster is relatively small, consisting of 300 galaxies. The cluster to which the Milky Way belongs, is called the → "Local Group".

Why are galaxies clustered together? Obviously the Creator grouped them in clusters, so that even the most distant reaches of the universe can proclaim His glory. At such a vast distance the light of a single galaxy is too dim to be detected on earth, but a cluster can be observed. The words of the psalmist: "Like your name, O God, your praise reaches to the ends of the earth" (Ps 48:10), are also valid for the most distant points of the universe, as is clear from known astronomical facts.

Today the total number of stars in the observable universe is estimated to be 10^{25} (10 followed by 24 zeros). Nobody knows the actual number. We read in one of the apocryphal books:

> "We have seen only a few of His works, the Lord Himself having made all things – and having given wisdom to devout men" (Sira 43:36-37)[5].

What does the Bible say about the number of stars? Jeremiah writes: "...as countless as the stars of the sky and as measureless as the sand on the seashore" (Jer 33:22). At that time, when scientists were convinced that there were only about 3,000 stars, Jeremiah wrote that nobody would be able to count the stars. Let us consider an imaginary dialogue between Jeremiah (J) and a well-known astronomer (A) of that day (the seventh century before Christ):

A: Jeremiah, you write about the number of stars as if you knew what you were saying. My colleagues and I have studied astronomy for a long time and daily concern ourselves with the stars. Our researches have

---

5 **Sira**, or 'Ecclesiasticus' in *The Jerusalem Bible*: This is one of the apocryphal Old Testament books (Greek: *apókryphos* = concealed, secret, not genuine). Such books are not regarded as the words of God and have not been included with the canonical books of the Bible [G5, p 127 - 129]. *Martin Luther* characterised these books as not part of Holy Scripture, but useful and profitable to read. Such quotations are sometimes pertinent to our theme.

made astronomy the most advanced science. Even kings appreciate and respect our findings.

J: You may have discovered many things, but you are mistaken about the number of stars.

A: How do you know that? You have not studied astronomy, not even for a single semester. So do not speak about matters which you do not understand!

J: Yes, of course my studies were in a totally different field. But I still maintain that nobody is able to count the stars, because they total such a large number, similar to the number of grains of sand on the beach.

A: We have recently completed a survey of the number of stars in the sky, employing our younger colleagues whose vision is sharp and unimpaired. They did not miss any stars, and their count was 3,000. Revise your biblical text; it has been disproved by our scientific findings.

J: I still maintain that I have written the truth. I am no expert, but I know Him Who created the stars. He has told me and I believe Him.

It is noteworthy that only now in the twentieth century we can fully appreciate the astronomical import of biblical affirmations. It behoves us to trust biblical pronouncements in other cases as well. Let us now try to visualise the above-mentioned number of stars. No human being lives long enough to count such a large number, so we use a computer, one of the fastest ones available[6]. It can do ten

---

6 **Computer:** One of the fastest computers is the series C-90 CRAY C916/16. It has 16 processors and its speed is approximately 10 GFLOPS (= 10 Giga FLOPS). FLOPS indicate the number of Floating Point Operations Per Second; 10 Giga FLOPS means that ten thousand million arithmetical calculations like addition and multiplication can be done in one second. At present super computers last about five years, and the above-mentioned CRAY computer could only count 1.5 thousand millionth percent of the number of stars in five years.

thousand million calculations in one second, which is extremely fast! But even at this great speed it would require 30 million years of non-stop counting stars, and indeed, no computer could last as long as that. God has foretold the result of such an endeavour through His prophet Jeremiah: "...as countless as the stars of the sky and as measureless as the sand on the seashore" (Jer 33:22).

Isaiah tells us that God's thoughts and ways are far higher than ours (Isaiah 55:8,9). Not only are His thoughts higher than ours, they are also much faster. He can count the stars! And He has done exactly that; He even gave each one a name: "He determines the number of the stars and calls them each by name" (Ps 147:4). The very next verse emphasises His greatness: "Great is our Lord and mighty in power; his understanding has no limit." This is also proclaimed by Isaiah:

> "Lift your eyes and look to the heavens: Who created all these? He who brings out the starry host one by one, and calls them each by name. Because of his great power and mighty strength, not one of them is missing" (Isaiah 40:26).

Johann Hey (1789 – 1854) wrote the following song full of wisdom:

> "Do you know how many stars shine in the night?
> Do you know how many clouds float in the sky?
> Not a single star or cloud escapes God's sight.
> He has counted all of them, need we ask why?"

The Creator takes note of each and every star, without the use of a computer or a telescope, and in one second. For Him anything is possible! And yet He is also concerned about each and every human being. This is clearly expressed in Psalm 8:3-4:

> "When I consider your heavens, the work of your fingers, the moon and the stars, which you have set

in place, what is man that you are mindful of him, the son of man that you care for him?"

In contrast, other world views paint a dreary and dismal picture. *F. M. Wuketits*, for example, writes [W6, p 40]: "The universe is as deaf to our lamentations as to our exuberant expressions of joy. Nobody out there in the infinite reaches of the cosmos will be sad when a certain species concludes its process of self-extermination. I am sorry, but this is the only conclusion I could publish about the evolution of thought." Similarly false is *Kant's* conclusion that the immeasurably large universe destroys our importance. If he had believed some of the verses of Psalm 8, he would have reached quite a different conclusion about our position in this vast universe.

We are not cosmic outcasts (*F. Nietzsche:* "kosmische Eckensteher"), neither are we "gypsies at the edge of the universe" [*J. Monod*, M1, p 151]. On the contrary, we are beloved by our Father in heaven, through Jesus Christ.

Heinz Kaminski (1921), for many years director of the Bochum Observatory, was once asked what his thoughts were when he first pointed his telescope at the moon, the planets, and the Milky Way. Was he also looking for the solution of the puzzle like *Einstein*? He gave the following revealing answer [H7, p 106-107]:

> "We will not find the solution of the puzzle out there in the universe, but in ourselves. This gigantic 'something' enters our brain through the pupils, where it begins to grow. What a fantastic event. Astronomers have reduced man to an atomic nothing; he was continuously dragged out and left to stand alone like a worm at seventeen thousand million light-years. He is overwhelmed by the enormous stars and vast distances. To himself he appears tiny and insignificant. Clever people have

forgotten that this puny human being occupies an important place in the eye of the Creator, as can be read in the Bible. When God had created the earth, He found that something was lacking; there was nobody who could appreciate His works and acknowledge His might. Then He created man and gave him some crumbs of the greatness of his own Spirit. And these crumbs enable us to grasp something of the logistics of the entire system. If we did not carry this creative spark, we would not have been able to analyse the laws of the universe nor understand their effects."

The universe in its immensity was especially created for us humans so that we could see and appreciate the glory and the power of God. He is so great that it required no more effort to create ten stars than one, or one thousand, or even 10^{25}. He did not exert Himself, neither did He perspire. His creative words were sufficient: "For He spoke, and it came to be; He commanded, and it stood firm" (Ps 33:9).

3. In What Respects Do the Stars Differ?

Are not all stars similar? A superficial glance might lead to this conclusion, but investigations have revealed that all stars are different, just as no two snowflakes are alike (see *Figures 1* and *2*). Astronomers typify stars by many different characteristics: Mass, luminosity, radius, temperature, spectral class, average density, average emission of energy per unit volume and per second, gravitational acceleration at the surface, speed of rotation, magnetic field, and chemical composition. There is a very wide range of stellar properties which will now be illustrated by means of some extreme cases. See Footnote 4 for some remarks on the estimated distances of the stars and galaxies.

1. The nearest star: Apart from the sun itself, the nearest star to earth at 4.28 light years away is *Proxima Centauri* (Latin: *proximus* = nearest), but it cannot be seen by the unaided eye. It is also known as *Alpha Centauri C* and is so far away that a space ship travelling at a speed of 100,000 km per hour, would require 46,000 years to get there (see Chapter 4, model 2). Being a variable star, its apparent brightness lies between 9.7 and 10.7 stellar magnitudes, while its maximum absolute magnitude is 15.1. It is one of the three components of Alpha Centauri in the constellation *Centaurus* in the southern sky. The two bright companions, having apparent magnitudes of 0.3 and 1.7, are only slightly farther from the earth. Their absolute magnitudes are 5.7 and 4.4 respectively. As seen from earth, Alpha Centauri is the third brightest star. It is one of the "Pointers" pointing at the Southern Cross (see chapter 8.3.3).

2. The most distant star: The quasar denoted *PKS 2000-330*, was discovered in 1982 by two Australian astronomers, *A. Wright* and *D. Jauncey*. At that time it was regarded as the most distant known object at an estimated 12 thousand million light-years. But Quasar *Q1208011*, discovered in the constellation *Virgo* (the Virgin), appears to be some 400 million light-years further.

3. The seemingly brightest star: As seen from earth, *Sirius* is the brightest, having an apparent magnitude of −1.47, which is equal to one 50 millionth of the sun's brilliance. Its absolute brightness is 26 times that of the sun whose apparent magnitude is −26.7. Sirius has a diameter of 4.8 million km and at 8.7 light-years it is the sixth closest star system. Being in the constellation *Canis Major* (the Great Dog), it is known as *Alpha Canis Majoris*, and it can be seen predominantly in the southern hemisphere.

4. The star with the greatest absolute magnitude: *Eta Carinae* is a variable star at a distance of 6,400 light-years. Stars of which the emitted amount of light, or some other property, changes over a period of several years or less, are known as variable stars. In 1843 it became the second brightest star after Sirius when its apparent magnitude increased to −1. Its absolute brightness flared up to four

Figures 1 and 2: *Snowflakes. All snowflakes are hexagonal, varying in size from one to three mm. Their weight varies from one-half milligram down to one-200th of a mg. It has been proved mathematically that every single snowflake is unique; the same pattern is never repeated. The size and shape of the crystals of ice depend mainly on the temperature and the amount of water vapour available as they develop. At temperatures above −40 °C, ice crystals form around minute particles of dust or chemical substances that float in the air; at lower temperatures, crystals form directly from water vapour. If the air is humid, the crystals tend to grow rapidly, develop branches, and clump together to form snowflakes. In colder and drier air, the particles remain small and compact.*

million times that of the sun. This means that if the sun and Eta Carinae were at the same distance from the earth, it would be 4 million times as bright as the sun. If the sun was removed to a distance of 6,400 light-years, its apparent magnitude would be 70, and it would be unobservable, even by the most powerful telescope, as only stars brighter than magnitude 23 can be observed. At a distance of 55 light-years, it would be barely visible as a magnitude 6 star. The present apparent magnitude of Eta Carinae is 7, which makes it invisible to the naked eye. It is, however, the brightest infra-red source in the sky at a wavelength of 20 μm. It is located in the constellation *Carina*, the Keel (of the ship), in the southern hemisphere.

5. The brightest star in the northern hemisphere: The brightest star in the northern celestial sphere is *Arcturus (= Alpha Bootes)* which has an apparent magnitude of − 0.04. It is the fourth brightest star.

6. The dimmest star: The absolute brightness of the star designated as *RG 0050-2722* in the southern constellation, the Sculptor, has an absolute brightness of 19. Its surface temperature is 2,600 °C, its mass only 2.3 % that of the sun, and its distance is 80 light-years.

7. The brightest globular cluster in the northern sky: In the constellation of Hercules a star cluster catalogued as *M13*, consists of 500,000 single stars at a distance of 22,500 light-years. It is the brightest cluster in the northern hemisphere; only two clusters in the southern sky, *Omega Centauri* and *47 Tucanae*, are brighter.

8. The brightest galaxy: The galaxy with the largest absolute magnitude is the elliptical nebula *M87* in *Virgo*. With a brightness of − 21.7, it surpasses the Andromeda galaxy's absolute magnitude of − 21.1 by 42 %.

9. The largest star: The largest known star is *Alpha Herculi* or *Ras Algethi*. It is accompanied by a double star. Its dia-

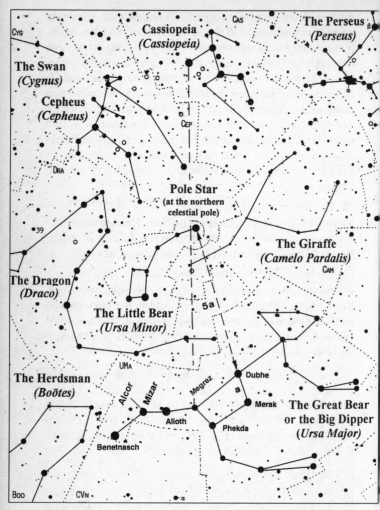

Figure 3: *View of the northern sky at 9.00 p. m. (Central European time) on November 15. The connected dots indicate the different constellations (based on* Sterne und Weltraum *{Stars and Space}, 11/1991).*

meter, including an expanding gas cloud around its main component, is about 250 thousand million km. Some comparisons might give a better idea of its immense size: This measure is 180,000 times the diameter of the sun, or 1,672 times the distance from the earth to the sun, or 21 times the average diameter of our solar system, which measures 11,800 million km, including the orbit of Pluto. The *Voyager 1* space probe achieved its maximum speed of 40,000 km per hour when it passed near Jupiter. At this speed it would take 17 years to cover the distance from the sun to Pluto, and 700 years to cross the Alpha Herculi system.

10. The smallest star: The white dwarf star, *LP 327-16*, is approximately half the size of the moon, having a diameter of only 1,700 km. It was discovered in 1962 at a distance of 100 light-years.

11. The most massive star: Called *Plaskett's Star*, the most massive star is situated in the constellation known as the *Unicorn (Monoceros)*. It is a double star discovered in 1922 by a Canadian, *John S. Plaskett*, and is designated *HD 47 129*. Each component of this supergiant star (type O7) has a mass equal to 55 times that of the sun, while the sun's diameter could fit 25 times into the radius of the primary star.

12. The best-known binary star: When two stars are so close together that they can only be distinguished by the aid of a telescope, they are called a double star or a binary system. In an optical binary there is no physical connection between the two components; they just appear to be close together in the line of sight. One of them may be much further from the earth than the other. On the other hand, the components of a physical binary star revolve about their common centre of gravity; they are gravitationally linked together. The best-known binary star is *Mizar (Zeta Ursae Majoris)*. In 1650 *G. B. Riccioli* discovered that it had two components. It is the second last star in the "handle" of the Big Dipper, and a small telescope can separate the two constituents. Their angular separation is 14.4″. Just above *Mizar* a fifth magnitude star, *Alcor*, can be seen. Together with Alcor, Mizar constitutes an optical binary star with an angular separation of 11′50″. In reality they are separated by 22 light-years.

13. The largest galaxy: Probably the largest galaxy of the universe is *Markarian 348*, discovered in 1987 with a very large radio telescope in New Mexico. Having a diameter of 1.3 million light-years, it is 13 times as large as our Milky Way galaxy. It is located at a distance of 300 million light-years from earth in the direction of the Andromeda nebulae.

14. The largest galaxy in the Local Group: With its diameter of 150,000 light-years, the *Andromeda* galaxy in the constellation with the same name, is the largest member of the → Local Group. Also designated as *M31* and *NGC 224*, its total mass is estimated as being 310 thousand million times that of the sun. The Milky Way is the second largest galaxy in this group, and the Triangle nebula *M33* located in the constellation *Triangulum* follows as third largest. The latter is half the size of the Milky Way and consists of ten thousand million stars. The plane of Andromeda makes an angle of 77° with the line-of-sight from the earth.

15. The most distant galaxy in the Local Group: At a distance of 4.1 million light-years, IC10, is regarded as a member of the → Local Group.

16. The nearest and furthest galaxies: The two *Clouds of Magellan*, visible near the southern celestial pole, are about 165,000 light-years distant. The *Greater M. Cloud* is located in the *Swordfish*, and the *Lesser M. Cloud* can be seen in *Tucan*.

With the largest ever red shift factor ($z = 3.8$), galaxy 4C41.17 (Fourth Cambridge Catalogue) is regarded as the most distant galaxy. Its distance is estimated at 12 thousand million light-years, the highest value for a galaxy, by astronomers *George K. Miley* (Leiden, Holland) and *Kenneth C. Chambers* (Honolulu, Hawaii).

17. The Great Wall: *Margaret J. Geller* and *John P. Huchra*, astrophysicists of the Harvard-Smithsonian Centre for Astrophysics in Cambridge, created a sensation. Trying to obtain a 3-D picture of their distribution, they had investigated about 15,000 galaxies by 1989. A computer printout revealed the existence of a "wall" of galaxies, approximately 500 million light-years long, 200 million light-years wide, and only 15 million light-years thick. They called this cluster extending from a distance of 470 to 600 million light-years, "The Great Wall". Galaxies usually appear to cluster on the surface of gigantic spheres (called "Hubble-bubbles"), so that the discovery of this "wall" was quite a surprise. As seen from the earth, the Great Wall extends from the constellation Cancer, through the Small Lion, Berenice's Hair, Bootes, and the Northern Crown, with its furthest edge in Hercules.

18. The fastest pulsar: → Pulsar *PSR 1937 + 214* was discovered in 1982 by *Donald Backer*, a radio astronomer. Situated in the constellation The Fox (Latin: *Vulpecula*), it rotates at a speed of 642 revolutions per second. Every point on its equator moves at the furious speed of 39,000 km per second. The speed of points on the earth's equator is by comparison only 460 m per second. The period of the pulses of this pulsar is exactly 1.55806449023 milliseconds (one 642nd of a second) – a new record of astronomical precision.

19. The most dense astronomical objects: "Black holes" are the most remarkable objects in the universe. They absorb light as well as matter, and are invisible. We can only detect the radiation of collapsing gases in their vicinity. The internal density of a black hole is about 10^{17} g per cubic cm; matter cannot be more densely packed than this. If the earth could be compressed to this density, it would be the size of a ping-pong ball. A pin-head sized chunk of a black hole would weigh 420 million tonnes on earth. More than two million 25-metre steam locomotives of 200 tonnes each would be required to equal such a weight. If these locomotives were lined up, they would form a train 51,000 km long, a distance greater than the circumference of the earth.

A very large black hole was discovered in the centre of galaxy NGC 3115 in 1992 by the American astronomers *D. Richstone* and *J. Kormendy*. At a distance of 30 million light-years, it seems to be 100 times as massive as any previously investigated black hole, and it could easily contain a thousand million solar masses and is approximately 30 million light-years away from the Earth.

20. Moving star clusters: Ancient astronomers believed that the positions of the stars were fixed, but stars and constellations are constantly on the move. *Edmund Halley* (1656 – 1742) was the first to discover that individual stars are in motion (1718). Because they are so far away, changes in their position can only be noticed after several centuries. After a few thousand years the present constellations will look quite different.

The fact that some stars travel together in clusters, has only recently been discovered. Only a few such groups are known (the Pleiades, the Hyades , Praesepe, Ursa major moving cluster ("Bärenstrom" in German)). The stars in such a group not only lie fairly close together, but they also travel in the same direction. It is noteworthy that the Bible mentions this property of the Pleiades: "Can you bind the beautiful Pleiades? Can you loose the cords of Orion?" (Job 38:31).

Every single star and galaxy has its unique characteristics as determined by God:

> "The sun has one kind of splendour, the moon another and the stars another; and star differs from star in splendour (Greek: *doxa*)" (1 Cor 15:41).

Stars differ in luminosity as scientifically indicated in the *Hertzsprung-Russel* diagram where they are distributed according to temperature and spectral class. In addition, each star is significant in its glorification of God. We read in the apocryphal book of Sira: "The glory of the stars makes the beauty of the sky, a brilliant decoration to the height of the Lord. At the words of the Holy One they stand as He decrees, and never grow slack at their watch" (Sira, or Ecclesiasticus 43:9-11). And in the book of Job there are several references to the stars and to the fact that God has endowed them with structures some of which we can study and others remain unfathomable:

> "He alone stretches out the heavens and treads on the waves of the sea. He is the Maker of the Bear and Orion, the Pleiades and the constellations of the south. He performs wonders that cannot be fathomed, miracles that cannot be numbered"
>
> (Job 9:8-10).

4. How Big is the Universe?

The immense distances encountered in space are difficult to visualise. Even the distances to the nearest stars cannot be illustrated in earthly terms. In an attempt to describe some aspects of space in our vicinity, we now present four models to readers who like dabbling with numbers.

Model No 1: In our first model everything is reduced to one hundred thousand millionth (10^{11}) of its actual size. Using this scale 1 cm represents one million km, so that the 1.392 million km diameter of the sun is reduced to 14 mm, the size of a cherry. The earth would then be the size of a grain of sand, 1.5 m from the cherry. Jupiter would be 8 m from the cherry-sun and its size would be 1.4 mm. Pluto, with a diameter of 0.05 mm would be found at a distance of 59 m. The nearest star, *Alpha Centauri,* would be 410 km distant, and *Barnard's star* 560 km from the cherry-sun. The distance to the Andromeda galaxy (2.3 million actual light-years) would already extend beyond the earth. It would be 1.5 times the distance from the earth to the sun, and the largest distance we considered, the 12,400 million light-years mentioned in Chapter 3 No 2, would be 7,800 times the actual earth-sun distance. It is clear that this model is inadequate when it comes to these incomprehensibly vast astronomical distances.

Model No 2: Another method of representing the immeasurable size of the universe is by considering space voyages. Unmanned space probes have already travelled to various planets in the solar system. *Voyager 1* was launched on 5 September 1977 and *Voyager 2* a few weeks earlier on 20 August. They were meant to traverse the solar system and then leave it forever. *Voyager 2* passed Jupiter on 9 July 1979, Saturn on 12 November 1981, and Uranus on 24 January 1986. Neptune was photographed on 25 August 1989, and two previously unknown satellites were discovered. Although travelling at the speed of light, the radio waves covered the distance from Neptune back to the earth in four hours and six minutes. Let us embark on an imaginary space voyage at a speed of 100,000 km per hour, which, although double that of *Voyager* 2, is a mere ten thousandth of the speed of light. Travelling at this speed, it would require 46,000 years to reach Proxima Centauri (see Chapter 3 No 1), and another 46,000 years for the return journey. Thus even the very nearest star is so far away that it is humanly impossible to go there.

Model No 3: Suppose that a man could be made as small as an atom of hydrogen. Then would the entire population of the earth require a room, a matchbox, a thimble, or the head of a pin? The actual result is astounding: A bacterium measuring about 2 to 3 thousandths of a millimetre, could contain the total population of 1,000 earths! At this scale the earth itself would measure only one millimetre, the moon 0.3 mm, and the sun 110 mm. The earth-sun distance would then be reduced to 12 m, while Saturn, at a distance of 111 m, would have a diameter of 9 mm. The distance to Proxima Centauri would be equal to the distance from Frankfurt to Tel Aviv. Rigel, the brightest star in Orion, would lie 50,000 km beyond the moon.

Model No 4: We conclude our representations with a fourth experiment. The diameter of the well-known Andromeda galaxy is 150,000 light-years. If you take a postcard-sized photograph of Andromeda and push a pin through it, the diameter of the hole would represent 600 light-years. A jet plane travelling at a speed of 1,000 km/h would require an unbelievable 650 million years to cross this gap!

Contemplation of the distances and sizes in the universe takes us to the limits of our imagination and our comprehension. In the humble words of Job: "Can you fathom the mysteries of God? Can you probe the limits of the Almighty? They are higher than the heavens – what can you do? They are deeper than the depths of the grave – what can you know?" (Job 11:7-8). In awesome wonder we can agree with the psalmist: "How great are your works, O Lord, how profound your thoughts!" (Ps 92:5).

Another interesting fact is the similarity between the very large, the macro-cosmos, and the very small, the micro-cosmos. We cannot really grasp either of them, but the following models may help.

Model A: At breakfast this morning you might have sprinkled a pinch of salt on a boiled egg. Do you know the number of atoms in a single grain of salt? Our life span is far too short to count this number, so once more we require a super computer (see Chapter 2). It can count 10 thousand million numbers per second, but even so the atoms in one single grain of salt would keep it occupied for 50 years.

Model B: If we enlarge every atom of our grain of salt to the size of a pinhead, its volume would increase to 400,000 times the pyramid of Cheops. And if we spread all these pinheads evenly over the continent, Europe would be covered to a depth of 20 cm.

Model C: In the next chapter we will see that space is not characterised by matter, but by emptiness. The same emptiness is found in atoms. If the proton in the nucleus of a hydrogen atom was enlarged to the size of a pinhead and placed in Frankfurt, Germany, the orbit of the electron in the atom would run through Italy, France, Denmark, and Poland.

5. Four Characteristics of Space

We read in Job 26:7: "He (God) spreads out the northern [skies] over empty space; He suspends the earth over nothing."

This is a remarkable astronomical statement, which may be expressed in present-day terms as follows:

"Space is dark and empty, and the earth floats freely without any visible support."

Considering the time at which this verse was written, its significance in terms of present-day astronomy is profound. Job is regarded as one of the oldest books of the Bible, and it was written at a time when it was believed that the earth was a flat disk floating on water, with the firmament to which the stars were fixed, enclosing it from above. The authors of the Bible, however, did not subscribe to the primitive world-view of their Babylonian and other neighbours. In the Name of God Job wrote about three aspects of reality, the truth of which could only be fully understood in the twentieth century:

1. Space is empty: The mass of individual stars is so large that we cannot really comprehend it. The mass of each of the two components of Plaskett's star (HD 47 129, a binary) is 55 times that of the sun, or 18.4 million times that of the earth. Earth's mass is close to an enormous 6×10^{24} kg, and the total mass of all the stars in the Milky Way galaxy is equal to that of 200 thousand million suns. Faced by such vast numbers, the statement that space is empty, sounds facetious. But if we consider the immense distances which separate these enormous masses (see Chapter 4), the relationships discussed here, should be acceptable.

Let us consider the situation in our Milky Way galaxy: On average, one sun is found in a volume of 350 cubic light-years. One cubic light-year is a cube with each edge equal to one light-year and its volume is 8.47×10^{38} cubic km or 6×10^{20} times the volume of the sun. This means that the average density of the Milky Way is 7×10^{-23}g per cubic cm. Keep in mind that 70 % of all the visible matter in the universe is hydrogen, the simplest and lightest element. And most of the remainder consists of helium, the second lightest element. Then it makes sense to use hydrogen for the purpose of comparison. The mass of one atom of hydrogen is 1.6618×10^{-24}g, so that if the mass of the Milky Way were spread out evenly through the space it occupies, there would only be forty hydrogen atoms per cubic cm. Under normal earth conditions one cubic cm of air contains approximately 27×10^{18} molecules, and the best vacuum that can be obtained in the laboratory (in a very small volume at the very low temperature of liquid helium), is a pressure of 10^{-12} Pascal[7]. Such a vacuum still contains 270 molecules per cubic cm. This means that the average density of the Milky Way with its 200 thousand million stars is "thinner" by a factor ten than that of the highest vacuum that can be obtained on earth. If the galaxies are regarded as "islands" of matter and their density is so low already, then inter-galactic space as a whole is even emptier. The estimates of different authors vary between 10^{-31} and 10^{-34}g per cubic cm. In conclusion, we can state that the universe is on the average 700 million times "emptier" than the already very empty space within our galaxy. The biblical affirmation in Job 26:7 is very modern!

---

7 **Pascal:** The Pascal was accepted as the international unit of pressure (SI = *Système International d'Unités;* International System of Units) at the fourteenth *General Conference on Weights and Measures* in 1971. When a force of one Newton is exerted on one square metre, the resultant pressure is one Pascal (1 $Pa = 1 \ N/m^2$). One bar = 0.1 MPa (Mega-pascal) = 10^5 Pa. The Pascal is a very much smaller unit than the previously used 1 atmosphere (1 atm = 101,325 Pa).

2. Space is dark: Apart from moonlit nights, it is obvious that the night sky is dark. Astronauts on their way to the moon saw the earth as a blue pearl against a black background. But our night sky is not really dark. The dim light pervading the night is the result of two effects:

(a) The airglow coming from the upper layers of the atmosphere, caused by the X-rays of the sun, and

(b) Diffuse illumination by the Milky Way.

Both of these sources of light can be ascribed to our special position in space, near the sun, and being located in the Milky Way galaxy. Space is utterly dark when one moves away from the vicinity of the stars and the galaxies. If the earth had no atmosphere, the sky would be pitch black, even at noon. But it is blue because the atmosphere scatters light with short wave-lengths. Job 26:7 has once more been shown to be very accurate. And we also read in Isaiah 50:3: "I clothe the sky with darkness." Today we know that the *Andromeda Galaxy* is the only stellar object outside our galaxy which is visible to the unaided eye. All other visible stars and nebulae belong to our local Milky Way galaxy. The only reason why we do see stars, is that we are located inside this galaxy. It would be very different if our solar system was situated in deep space, far away from any galaxy. Then we would not see a single star, and we would be surrounded by the unimaginable blackness of inter-galactic space. Only with the aid of sophisticated telescopes could we have discovered the existence of very distant faint objects, the remote galaxies. An observer placed at random in deep space, would in general not be fortunate enough to be near a galaxy, because the universe mostly comprises empty space, and galaxies are precious rarities. Like ourselves, any observer finding himself close to or inside a galaxy, could regard himself as being privileged. If our solar system were located in another galaxy, our night sky would be completely different.

3. The earth is suspended by nothing: The earth does not lie on anything, neither is it attached to anything – it floats in space. Only in 1687 did *Isaac Newton* (1643 – 1727) succeed in describing the motion of the earth in its orbit, by means of the law of gravity which he had discovered. The exact and correct description of the Bible was expressed in mathematical terms in his book *Philosophiae Naturalis Principia Mathematica*. *Kepler* (1571 – 1630) had previously formulated his three laws of planetary motion, and it was found that all three of them could be deduced from *Newton's* general law of gravitation. With a few exceptions, the motions of all objects in the universe can be described by means of this general law.

4. Space is fundamentally unfathomable: The actual structure of space has not yet been unravelled. It is one of the great unanswered but at the same time most fascinating questions of astronomy. *Giordano Bruno* (1548 – 1600) and *Edmund Halley* (1656 – 1742) were of the opinion that space was infinite. But according to *Olbers'* Paradox[8] space cannot be infinite. Present-day views, based on non-Euclidean geometry (curved space) and *Einstein's* general theory of relativity, regard space as finite but unbounded. *Otto Heckmann* (born 1901) expressed himself as follows [H2, p 129, 134]: "The ingenuity of man's mind is definitely not limited, so that a relatively large number of world-views have been produced, so large ... that the number of cosmological theories is inversely proportional to the number of known facts ... Observational data becomes steadily less accurate, and eventually it becomes meaningless because of the limited power of our instru-

---

8 **Olbers' paradox:** *H. W. M. Olbers* (1758 – 1840), a German physician and astronomer of Bremen, proved mathematically that if the universe was infinite and the number of stars was infinite, then the night sky should be infinitely bright. For him it was an inexplicable paradox that the night sky was black, and the only possible conclusion was that the universe could not be infinite.

ments." *Volker Weidemann,* a German astrophysicist from Kiel, came to the conclusion that the universe is fundamentally incomprehensible. His scientific findings compelled him to write:

> "Cosmology is based on more philosophical assumptions than all other branches of science. If we are forced to define the boundaries of that which can be called science and cannot hope to answer fundamental cosmological questions scientifically, then we must concede that the universe is basically incomprehensible. Science must acknowledge that there are questions that cannot be answered. The rest is epistemological theory."

In Jeremiah 31:37 the Bible a long time ago already stated that the structure of the universe could not be researched, neither could the interior of the earth: "Only if the heavens above can be measured and the foundations of the earth below be searched out ..." The Bible manifests itself as a book of truth, encompassing all astronomical facts.

6. Why Were the Stars Created?

This question – the purpose of the stars – is answered more than once in the Bible. We will return to the previously mentioned Psalm 19:1-6 later, but the creation account itself is most explicit. We read in Genesis 1:14-19:

> "And God said, 'Let there be lights in the expanse of the sky to separate the day from the night, and let them serve as signs to mark seasons and days and years, and let them be lights in the expanse of the sky to give light on the earth.' And it was so. God made two great lights – the greater light to govern the day and the lesser light to govern the night. He also made the stars. God set them in the expanse of the sky to give light on the earth, to govern the day and the night, and to separate light from darkness. And God saw that it was good. And there was evening, and there was morning – the fourth day."

Three assertions can be clearly distinguished:

The heavenly bodies were created to

 – shine on the earth as sources of light and energy,

 – determine times and seasons,

 – serve as signs or messengers.

These three functions indicate unequivocally that all astronomical bodies were made for the purpose of serving the earth; more specifically: to serve mankind. From these purposes given at creation, the chronological order of creation (earth on the first day and all the other planets only on the fourth day), as well as the overall testimony of the Bible, we conclude: **From a biblical point of view we cannot expect life to exist on the other planets of our so-**

lar system, nor yet on planets in any other galaxies, should such planets be proven to exist.

In 1900 the *French Academy of Science* put up a prize of 100,000 francs for anybody who would be the first to establish communication with extra-terrestrial beings, excluding the planet Mars. They were so sure of life on Mars that contact with its inhabitants was not regarded as worthy of a prize. But it can be stated positively that no "little green men" exist, either on Mars or anywhere else. Although there are absolutely no concrete indications that extra-terrestrial life exists, many evolution-biased astronomers, impressed by the vast numbers of stars, believe that life must have evolved on other planets as it is presumed to have happened on earth. This question is discussed more fully in [G4, p 195-202]. The SETI scientists in America (SETI = Search for Extra-Terrestrial Intelligence) have conducted more than 48 experiments for detecting messages from space – but none of these was successful.

After this digression we shall now discuss the three above-mentioned functions of astronomical bodies.

6.1 The Stars Were Made to Shine on Earth

Without light there could be no life on earth. It is one of the essential prerequisites for life. This is why God made light on the first creation day. On the fourth day this light, which we cannot describe physically, was replaced by the sun. Photosynthesis is the process which makes life on earth possible; by its means the energy of sunlight is converted to chemical energy – chemical substances which can release this energy when required, are formed. The photosynthetic processes of plants is the first link in the energy chain of man and animal. This process is extremely ingenious, and no chemist or industrial engineer has as yet been able to duplicate it. It occurs generally in every blade of grass, even in the tiniest snippet, but this marvellous invention of the Creator remains a secret. The source of energy for all life on earth is thus the sun. Every year 200 thousand million tonnes of biomass grows on earth, and human consumption is about 1 % of this worldwide production.

Without the sun, no life on earth could be possible. It is the basic source of light and energy. "As the sun in shining looks on all things, so the work of the Lord is full of his glory. The Lord has not granted to the holy ones to tell of all his marvels which the Almighty Lord has solidly constructed for the universe to stand firm in his glory... The sun, as he emerges, proclaims at his rising, 'A thing of wonder is the work of the Most High!'... Great is the Lord who made him" (Sira 42:16-17; Sira 43:2,5).

It has been found that 75 % of the sun's total volume is hydrogen (H_2), 23 % helium (He), and 2 % heavier elements, while its upper layers contain 90 % hydrogen, 8 % helium, and 2 % other elements. It is probable that nuclear fusion processes occur in the sun's interior. When four hydrogen nuclei having an atomic weight of 1.008, collide, they combine to form one helium nucleus with atomic weight 4.003. There is therefore a loss of 4.032 (4 times 1.008) minus 4.003 atomic weights. This loss, 0.029 atomic masses, or 0.7 % (more accurately 0.719246 %) of the masses involved, is converted into energy. Conclusion: God's method of producing energy in his creation is by means of nuclear processes, or, more precisely, nuclear fusion.

When one gram of hydrogen is converted to 0.9928 g of helium according to the above equation, the mass loss of 7.2 mg is equivalent to 180 MWh[9], as derived from *Einstein's* formula $E = mc^2$. If we wanted to produce a similar

---

9 **MWh:** The Megawatt-hour is a unit of energy used in the generation of electrical power. The basic SI unit is the Watt (W), which is the power output when 1 Joule of energy is released per second. The following SI units are used:

amount of energy by burning coal, 22.1 tonnes of coal with a heat value of 2.93×10^7 Ws/kg would be required.

Every second about 655 million tonnes of hydrogen are converted to 650 tonnes of helium. This means that 4.3 million tonnes of the mass of the sun are converted to energy every second. This amounts to an unimaginable 3.4×10^{24} MWh per year. Less than one half thousandth of a millionth part of this energy reaches the earth (more accurately: 0.441×10^{-9}). At this rate 30 minutes is sufficient to supply all the energy requirements of the earth. The earth's annual energy consumption amounts to approximately 8,750 thousand million Megawatt-hours.

The sun radiates its energy profusely in all directions. The total amount of radiated energy, 3.86×10^{23} kilowatts, is regarded as the absolute luminosity of the sun. Every square centimetre of the sun's surface (total area 6.087×10^{22} cm^2) continuously radiates 6.35 kW of energy.

The amount of energy normally incident on one square metre (1 m^2 = 10,000 cm^2) of the earth's surface at the average earth-sun separation, is known as the $\rightarrow$ solar constant. This amounts to 1.395 kW/m^2, and it varies through a year, depending on the actual distance from the sun.

The distance from the earth to the sun, about 150 million km, is defined as one $\rightarrow$ astronomical unit (AU). One AU is 375,000 times the circumference of the earth at the equator, or 390 times the earth-moon distance. At a speed of 100 km/h a train would require 170 years to cover one AU, and a jet plane, doing 1000 km/h, would take 17 years. The fastest known speed is that of light. A ray of light emitted by the sun, requires 8 1/3 minutes to reach the

---

1 Watt-second (Ws) = 1 Joule (J) = 1 Newton-metre (Nm). And one Watt-hour is equivalent to 3600 Ws. One Megawatt-hour is one million times as much: 1 MWh = 10^6 Wh.

earth. The diameter of the sun is 1,392,000 km, which is 109 times that of the earth. And it would require 1,306,000 earths to make up the volume of the sun.

It is easy to realise that the Creator purposefully placed the earth at this distance from the sun. The actual temperatures prevailing on earth make life possible. A deviation of a few percent would have resulted in very different conditions. If the earth were nearer to the sun, it would have been too hot for life to exist, as in the case of Mercury and Venus. If it were further away, it would have been colder (Mars and Jupiter are too cold). Another important aspect as far as light and energy are concerned, is the inclination of the earth's axis. This inclination determines day-and-night cycles as well as the seasons, as discussed more fully in Appendix A1.1.

6.2 The Stars Were Made to Determine Times and Seasons

The first definition of a physical unit of measurement given in the Bible, is a time unit. Already on the first day before any stars existed, the diurnal cycle of night and day (evening and morning, darkness and light)[10] is defined. On the fourth day the sun and the stars were created to continue this cycle. The length of a day is determined by the speed of rotation of the earth with relation to the sun. The duration of the creation days is discussed more fully in [G3, p 33-55]. Not only are the creation events recorded in the Bible, but also the method for measuring their duration.

---

10 **Nomenclature:** The first entity named by God Himself, was the word for day (Gen 1:5). He also gave names to the night, heaven, the earth and the sea, as well as all the stars (Ps 147:4). But the animals were named by Adam (Gen 2:19-20).

In the present-day science of measurement (metrology) the units (for force, length, time, electrical current, etc) are defined by means of exactly repeatable physical processes. Only if there is such a standard, can other things be measured in a meaningful calibrated fashion. In a similar way the Creator gave us exact, astronomically tractable units of measurement: days, months, and years. The basic created cycles are:

1. The rotation of the earth: One → solar day, 24 hours, is defined as the time from noon to noon, when the sun passes the zenith on subsequent days. The actual duration of one complete revolution as measured against the stars, is a bit less than 24 hours, namely 23 h 56 min 4 s = 23.93444 hours. This is called a → sidereal day.

2. The Earth's Orbit around the Sun: The period of approximately 365.25 days required for one complete orbit is known as a sidereal year. Its actual length is 365 days 6 hours 9 minutes and 9 seconds = 365.2563547 days.

However, for the purpose of setting up an annual calendar, the duration from one vernal equinox[11] to the next in the northern hemisphere, is preferred. This usually occurs on March 21 (March 20 in leap years) when the sun crosses the equatorial plane from south to north – the beginning of spring. Because of the precession[12] of the earth's axis, this period, called a tropical year, is again shorter than a sidereal year. Its duration is 365 days

---

11 **Vernal equinox:** The equatorial plane of the earth makes an angle of 23 with the ecliptic. At the time of the vernal equinox the sun crosses the equatorial plane from south to north, and day and night have the same length at all places on earth. On September 23, the autumnal equinox, the sun crosses the plane of the equator from north to south. In the southern hemisphere the use of these terms is reversed.

12 **Precession** (Latin *praecedere* = march forward): The axis of the earth (imaginary line between the two poles) slowly revolves like the axis of an inclined top. It takes 25,700 years to complete one revolution.

5 hours 48 minutes and 46 seconds = 365.2421991 days, which is 0.3397222 hours = 20.383333 minutes shorter than a sidereal year.

3. The Moon's Orbit around the Earth: The length of a month is determined by the moon's orbit, as it goes through its phases from new moon to new moon. In the apocryphal book Sira we read (Chapter 46:6-8): "And then the moon, always punctual, to mark the months and make divisions of time: the moon it is that signals the feasts, a luminary that wanes after her full. The month derives its name from hers, she waxes wonderfully in her phases." The period from one phase to its next occurrence is 29.5 days. This so-called synodic month lasts exactly 29 days 12 hours 44 minutes 2.9 seconds = 29.530589 days. One complete revolution takes somewhat less time, the length of a sidereal month being 27 days 7 hours 43 minutes 11.5 seconds = 27.3216609 days. This is exactly equal to the period of the moon's rotation around its axis, so that we always see the same side of the moon.

By establishing years (365.2422 days) and months (29.5 days) the Creator provided basic time periods for our calendar. Our present Gregorian calendar is the result of centuries of trial and error:

One calendar year comprises 365 days divided into 12 months each lasting between 28 and 31 days. Every fourth year, which is known as a leap year, February has 29 days. But even this correction is insufficient to ensure that our calendar "keeps in step" with celestial motions. The following additional correction has been included: Centennial years like 1800 and 1900 are not leap years, but it is a leap year when it is divisible by 400, like the year 2000. In this way the average length of the year is decreased by 3/400 days = 0.0075 days out of 365.2425, so that, except for a difference of 26 seconds, our artificial calendar year corresponds to a natural solar or tropical year (between successive vernal equinoxes). This difference will add up to one day after a period of 3300 years.

The positions of the stars seem to be fixed with respect to time and point of observation. Conversely, measurement of the positions of the stars helps us to determine our position at sea, for example. Through the centuries the positions of the sun, the moon, and the stars have provided navigational information to sailors and explorers. Nowadays the GPS (Global Positioning System) employing radio signals transmitted by orbiting satellites, enables travellers to determine their position on earth by using equipment which measures the differences in the travel times of the radio signals from the various satellites.

We now come to an important feature of the stars: They are signs or messengers! Celestial objects have a God-given purpose. The following two questions now concern us and will be discussed next:

1. How do the stars transmit their messages?

2. What do they proclaim?

7. How Do the Stars Transmit their Messages

7.1 Their Messages Are Silent

God could have installed gigantic loudspeakers in space which could bombard us continually. Once, while travelling through Salt Lake City in America, I was confronted with loudspeakers set up for a Mormon conference. When I moved out of earshot of one loudspeaker, the next one could be heard immediately. One could not escape from this constant bombardment.

That is not God's method. The stars proclaim their message silently. God does not intrude on anybody, and He prefers to transmit his messages silently. We usually do it the other way round: The less we have to say, the louder we shout.

The important third verse of Psalm 19 can be understood in two ways:

1. The message of the stars reaches all peoples and nations: "There is no speech or language where their voice is not heard" (Ps 19:3). This means that there is no language group on earth which cannot understand the "speech" of the stars. Even people speaking different languages who cannot communicate directly with one another are addressed similarly by the stars. This message of God manifests itself continually wherever man goes.

The well-known evangelist, *C. H. Spurgeon*, once said: "Under the vast celestial firmament no person is beyond the reach of this messenger of God. One could easily escape from the light brought by an evangelist. But then such a person will find an accusing Nathan in the starlight, and a warning Jonah, or an admonishing Elijah. But for all believers the stars speak another language, stirring and lovely: The language of the living God Who wants to be their Father to Whom one could feel attracted and where one could be secure."

2. Message without words: "No utterance at all, no speech, no sound that anyone can hear" (*The Jerusalem Bible*, JB). Here it is emphasised that the message of the stars is transmitted without recourse to an articulated language or to spoken words; this voice is inaudible. "Yet their voice goes out through all the earth, and their message to the ends of the world" (Ps 19:4, JB). This specially coded message reaches everybody. Paul refers to Psalm 19 when he writes in Romans 10:18: "But I ask, Did they not hear? Of course they did: 'Their voice has gone out into all the earth, their words to the ends of the world'". The language of the stars can be compared to the silent sign language used by the deaf.

7.2 God's Message Can Be Understood by Anybody

The message proclaimed by the stars is universally accessible, to the illiterate as well as to the Nobel laureate. Anybody can read God's signature in creation. God's signs are available for everybody, irrespective of educational background, race, age, or locality. Even tribes not evangelised and living in the far corners of the earth can observe this transmission, according to Psalm 19:4: "Their voice goes out into all the earth, their words to the ends of the world."

7.3 God Uses a Code which Nobody Can Erase

Any program used in electronic data processing can be wiped out. If we want to get rid of a nasty letter, we can burn it. We could distance ourselves from the preaching of the gospel. We could destroy Bibles. Indeed, many countries do not allow Bibles to be imported. But the code of God written in the stars cannot be extinguished, neither can it be switched off like a radio receiver. Nothing can destroy God's messages. They outlast all times and eras, because they cannot wear away and no enemy can destroy them. God's witnesses in the sky cannot be muted by anybody[13]. They proclaim the gospel of the living God, continuously, unaffected by the multiplicity of human opinions.

---

13 **Stars and the Gospel:** God Himself will one day put an end to his celestial ministry. Jesus refers to such a time in Matthew 24:29: "Immediately after the distress of those days the sun will be darkened, and the moon will not give its light; the stars will fall from the sky, and the heavenly bodies will be shaken." At that time even God's word will become unavailable, as the prophet Amos (8:11-12) announced: "'The days are coming,' declares the Sovereign Lord, 'when I will send a famine through the land – not a famine of food or a thirst for water, but a famine of hearing the words of the Lord. Men will stagger from sea to sea and wander from north to east, searching for the word of the Lord, but they will not find it'." Just as there may come a day for every person when it will be too late, so there will also be a universal "too late".

8. What Do the Stars Proclaim?

8.1 Does the Universe Require a Creator?

Anybody can observe the starry skies from any place on earth, and this magnificent scene demands our attention and consideration. What is our conclusion? Poets have expressed their thoughts in prose and poetry and scientists use their technical vocabulary. Let us consider a few examples culled from the vast pool of different ideas.

Our Teutonic ancestors regarded the celestial sphere as a screen which separates the earth from the light-filled Valhalla. The stars were seen as holes through which the light shone down.

The German poet, *Jean Paul* (1763 – 1825), gave us the following pessimistic view in his novel, *Siebenkäs*:

> "I walked through the worlds, I ascended to the suns, and I flew along milky ways through the heavenly voids; but there is no God … Stark, mute nothing! Cold, everlasting fate! Frenzied chance! … How alone everybody is in the wide tomb of the universe!"

In his "Ode to joy" ("An die Freude") the well-known German poet *Friedrich von Schiller* (1759 – 1805) also considers God and the stars:

> "Let the inhabitants of the celestial sphere pay tribute to sympathy! It leads to the stars where the Great Unknown has his throne.
> …
> Do you fall down on your knees? Are you looking for the Creator? Look beyond the starry skies! He must live up there.
> …

> Let the saints stand closer, and take an oath on this
> golden wine to be true to the covenant, take your
> oath by the Ruler of the stars."

Schiller is gripped by the magnificence of the starry skies and cannot imagine that it could exist without the Creator. He knows neither who God is nor what He is like. He presumes Him to be far away – unreachable, beyond the universe containing the stars. He calls Him "the Great Unknown", because he did not know Him personally.

Steven Weinberg, one of the proponents of the "big bang" theory, wrote in 1977: "The more we understand about the universe, the less it seems to make sense" [W2, p 162].

In his new book about the dream of the unity of the universe (*Dreams of a Final Theory*) he discusses the search for God. After about 15 years he seems to be no closer to a solution and he is now resigned to the following opinion [W3, p 260]:

> "If there is a God who has special plans for hu-
> mankind, then He has gone out of his way to hide
> his interest in us. It seems to be impolite, if not
> disrespectful, to sanctify such a God with our
> prayers."

Weinberg himself realises where his thoughts lead when he concedes that the more we taylor our ideas of God to make Him more plausible, the less meaningful He becomes [W3, p 265]. We get the impression that *Weinberg* has never really heard anything about the God of the Bible. It is clear that he concerns himself with a "philosopher's god" when he laments [W3, p 254]:

> "Scientists and others often take the word 'God' to
> mean something so abstract and unconcerned that
> their god can barely be distinguished from the laws
> of nature. *Einstein* once said that he believed in the
> god of *Spinoza* who reveals himself in the systema-

tic harmony of that which exists, but he did not believe in a god who is concerned with the destinies and acts of human beings."

When you look for God in the ideas of philosophers, you will end up with a phantom-like spectre, but you will not discover the living and loving God whom you can know and worship and to whom you can pray personally.

Weinberg quotes *Jim Peebles*, an astrophysicist of Princeton University (America), agreeing with his statement that he believed that we simply are driftwood [W3, p 265].

Referring to the beginning of Psalm 19, *Weinberg* describes the stars as follows [W3, p 251]:

"Since the time of David the sun and the other stars have lost their singular status; we know that they are spheres of glowing gas, held together by the force of gravity, and prevented from collapsing by the pressure exerted by the heat of internal thermonuclear reactions. The stars do not tell us anything more or less about God than the stones lying on the ground. If there really were something that we could discover in nature that would provide us with a special insight into the work of God, then it would be the final natural laws."

Margaret Geller, an astronomer of Harvard, expresses similar views [W3, p 265]: "Why should it (the universe) be meaningful? What kind of meaning? It is merely and simply a physical system; where is its significance?"

How do we rate such reductionist thinking? *Weinberg* and *Geller* are like physicists who evaluate a *Bach* cantata or a violin recital only according to acoustical principles. It is true that every musical performance is based on exact physical laws where atmospheric and other conditions play a role. Wind instruments are tuned according to the density, pressure, and temperature of the air. No trumpet can be played in a vacuum, as the air serves as carrier for the sound vibrations. Since physical laws and certain ambient conditions are prerequisites for a musical performance, it is possible to describe the music in terms of frequencies and graphs of the sound waves. But the essential features of the music can neither be understood nor explained in this way. If you restrict yourself to such methods when evaluating a symphony for example, you miss the whole point; the meaning and the creative intent of the composer will completely escape you.

Investigations of the same stars and the same universe may lead to totally different conclusions. Through his studies of the *Greater Magellanic Cloud*, the French astronomer, *Charles Fehrenbach*, became internationally known in 1977. When reporter *Christian Chablais* asked him during an interview what the universe told him, his reply was:

> "Beholding hidden realities and understanding phenomena beyond the comprehension of others, causes increasing astonishment about the universe … As an astronomer, I do not find God in the cosmos. But I am a believing astronomer … astounded by the vast distances, the unboundedness, and the wonderful interplay of relationships among the stars, but also by the questions concerning the nature of the cosmos beyond the limits of observation."

When asked whether he agreed with the Psalmist that "The heavens declare the glory of God" (Ps 19:1), he replied:

> "Oh yes, I believe! And I would like to add that life itself as well as the atoms declare His glory. The significance of these words in the Bible has become even more important for our time" (from *C. Chablais*: *Dieu existe? Oui*, Paris 1979).

How is it possible to arrive at such diverging conclusions as those of *Weinberg* and *Fehrenbach*? The following story describes a similar situation:

One warm summer evening two people walk along the beach, listening to the whisperings of the lapping ripples, and watching the star-filled sky. Suddenly a light flashes out at sea. How do they respond?

The first one, a retired professor of physics, runs to his car where he keeps many physical instruments. He measures the duration of the flashes with a stop watch, determines the intensity of the light with a photometer, and analyses its spectrum. He also locates the position of the light against the starry background. On the way back home, he stops a couple of times to repeat the position readings.

Arriving home, his wife asks: "You seem to be excited, dear, did you see something unusual?"

"Yes", he replies. "I observed something which I could identify as a heated tungsten wire enclosed inside a silicate container. It radiated a regular set of flashes of visible light having an intensity of 2,500 lumen at a distance of about 850 meters from the coast."

The other person on the beach that evening is a young scout on his way home. When he arrives home, his mother asks the same question: "You seem to be excited, dear. Did you see something unusual?"

"Yes", he replies. "I saw a boat signalling SOS messages. So I called the coast guard and they immediately dispatched a rescue boat. Everybody on board was saved."

Which one of the two, who both observed the same events, evaluated the situation correctly? The first one could not rise above a description of the physical phenomenon, while the other one understood the meaning of the signals and acted accordingly. It is obvious that a similar divergence could be found when the stars are observed and studied.

In the northern winter of 1992/93 TIME carried a noteworthy article [W5] on the views of God entertained by American scientists. The self-acknowledged agnostic, *W. D. Hamilton*, an evolutionary biologist, stated quite vaguely: "The theological possibility is still certainly alive." TIME commented:

> "But 100 years ago, with *Darwin* (1809 – 1882) having shown how a long chain of tiny accidents happened to yield the human species, with metaphysics in retreat and the clockwork laws of classical physics ascendant, and with the universe's deft conduciveness to life still unfathomed, one might have thought 'the theological possibility' an unlikely survivor of the next century's science. That it should survive in such robust form would have seemed less likely still."

TIME referred to the admission that all scientists were confronted with an insurmountable barrier concerning the question of origins:

> "If you admit that we can't peer behind the curtain, how can you be sure there's nothing there?"

TIME set up the following balance sheet concerning all big bang hypotheses:

> "But 20th century science sketches a universe stranger than the one the deists imagined. It is a universe that seems not to run as predictably as a clock, a universe whose innermost workings may not be fathomable."

In Psalm 8:1-4 David describes a different viewpoint in his contemplation of creation, and his declaration of God's nearness:

"O LORD, our Lord, how majestic
is your name in all the earth!
You have set your glory above the heavens.
From the lips of children and infants
you have ordained praise because of your enemies,
to silence the foe and the avenger.
When I consider your heavens, the work of your
fingers,
the moon and the stars, which you have set in place,
what is man that you are mindful of him,
the son of man that you care for him?"

The American physicist *Heinz Pagels* asked [P1]:

"What is the universe? Is it a 3-D movie in which
we all are unwilling actors? Is it a cosmic joke, a
gigantic computer, a work of art of a higher Being,
or merely an experiment?"

Then he supplies an answer: "I believe that the universe is
a message encoded in a cosmic code, and it is the task of
the scientist to decipher this code." Let us take a closer
look at this aspect raised by *Pagels*.

Paul's Epistle to the Romans provides a fundamental
statement regarding the purpose of the stars and of the
entire creation. In Romans 1:19-21 the message of the stars
becomes clear. The created universe is definitely not
meaningless, because it serves an important purpose:

"Since what may be known about God is plain to
them, because God has made it plain to them. For
since the creation of the world God's invisible
qualities – his eternal power and divine nature –
have been clearly seen, being understood from
what has been made, so that men are without
excuse. For although they knew God, they neither
glorified Him as God nor gave thanks to Him, but
their thinking became futile and their foolish hearts
were darkened."

65

We can learn three things from this fundamental course directive:

1. The universe testifies to the existence of God: There is no nation on earth which does not in some way or other believe in a god. The testimony of creation is so clear that the vast cosmos could not have come into existence by chance. A Creator is patently required. It is God's will that we should react to His message. He told Abraham to look up at the heavens (Gen 15:5). This also applies to you and me: Behold the firmament; take the time to observe it; look through a telescope, and you will be greatly astonished. Some of God's majesty is revealed in the stars. A well-known physical law is the law of the conservation of energy. This fundamental law states that it is impossible to create energy out of nothing, neither can energy be destroyed. Where did the energy of the universe come from? It could not have created itself, and the only acceptable explanation is that it must have had an external source. God's creative acts provide the meeting point between faith and physical knowledge.

2. The universe bears witness to God's great power: The size of the cosmos is estimated to be at least 12 thousand million light-years. (Note that a light-year is a measure of distance, and not of time! One light-year is equal to a distance of 9.46 million million km). The total mass of all the matter in the universe is estimated to be 10^{54} kg. Using *Einstein's* energy equation, $E = mc^2$, the energy content of this mass is equal to 25×10^{60} MWh. When discussing the number of stars (10^{25}) we tried to give an impression of the enormous magnitude of this number. But the amount of energy in the universe is immeasurably beyond any possibility of an illustrative representation.

If you like dabbling with numbers, consider the following comparisons: The largest power generating plant on earth is Itaipu on the Paraña river (between Brazil and Paraguay). Its 18 turbines generate 12,600 MW. We may now calculate the total amount of energy that can be generated over a year: $E = P \times t$ (energy = power × duration) = 110.4×10^6 MWh per year. The ratio of 25×10^{60} to Itaipu's annual production is an incomprehensibly large number:

$$Z = 25 \times 10^{60} / (110.4 \times 10^6) = 0.23 \times 10^{54}$$
$$= 0.23 \times (1 \text{ thousand million})^6$$

Let us approach this number in steps. One square mm (mm^2) is the area of a tiny square with each side = 1 mm. Now we want to determine how many mm^2 can be placed on globes of various sizes. The surface area of a 12 mm cherry is 452 mm^2. That of a tennis ball is 13,000 mm^2, and a large pumpkin brings us to 800,000 mm^2. A sphere with a diameter of 1 meter has a surface area of 3.14 million mm^2. When its diameter is 100 m, the number of mm^2 reaches 31,400 million. But these numbers are still very small compared to Z, so that we require astronomical measurements:

Surface area of the earth	510×10^{18} mm^2
"Surface" of the sun	6.1×10^{24} mm^2
Area of a sphere containing the orbits of all the planets in the solar system	437×10^{30} mm^2
"Surface" of the largest star, Alpha Herculis (diameter 250,000 million km)	196×10^{33} mm^2
Surface of a sphere whose diameter is one light-year ($d = 9.46 \times 10^{18}$ mm)	281×10^{36} mm^2
Surface of a sphere whose diameter is 1000 light-years ($d = 9.46 \times 10^{21}$ mm)	281×10^{42} mm^2
Surface of a sphere whose diameter is one million light-years ($d = 9.46 \times 10^{24}$ mm)	281×10^{48} mm^2

The area of even such a gigantic sphere having a diameter of one million light-years is far too small to contain Z mm^2. This number is only reached when the diameter becomes approximately 28.4 million light-years.

How great and mighty must God then be when He simply spoke and such vast amounts of energy were created. Everything witnesses to the power of God which far surpasses all conceivable measures. Only God's "fingers" (Ps 8:3) were sufficient for his creative acts; He did not even use his hand. The astonished Psalmist cries out: "How many are your works, O LORD! In wisdom You made them all; the earth is full of your creatures" (Ps 104:24), and "Who can proclaim the mighty acts of the LORD or fully declare his praise?" (Ps 106:2).

The well-known French mathematician, *Blaise Pascal* (1623 – 1662), who founded probability calculus, stated that the works of creation require a decision from us: "Just as all things speak of God to those who know Him, and all things are revealed to those who love Him, just so they stay hidden from those people who do not seek Him and do not know Him."

The atheist *Theo Löbsack* is a striking example of such concealment: "Representations like these, that somewhere there is a mysterious reigning Being who is the First Cause of everything, where all the threads come together, who created the cosmos by his words and still governs everything – God – such representations could decorate a child's heaven." It seems that *Löbsack* does not know of the personal testimonies of great scientists when he restricts belief in the Creator to childish fancy. *Newton*, one of the greatest physicists ever, believed firmly that the solar system was created by God:

> "The wonderful relationships of the sun, the planets, and the comets could only have come into existence according to the plan and instructions of an omniscient and omnipotent Being."

In a similar vein the German astronomer, *Johann Heinrich Mädler* (1794 – 1874), concluded from his observations:

"A true scientist cannot be an atheist. When you peer so deeply into God's workshop and have so many opportunities to marvel at his omniscience and eternal order, as we have, then you should humbly bend your knees before the throne of the most holy God."

Johannes Kepler (1571 – 1630), the well-known German astronomer, also acknowledges God in his works, according to Romans 1:19-20. *Kepler* discovered the three laws of planetary motion named after him. In 1619 he described the third law in his work *Harmonices mundi*, and concluded with the following prayer, emphasising the union between scientific labours and personal faith in the Creator:

"This is what I wanted to discuss about the work of God the Creator. The time has now arrived that I finally lift up my eyes and my hands from these pages full of theorems and proofs towards heaven and attentively and humbly pray to the Father of Light: O Lord, You who through the light we see in nature and the light of your mercy, work in us the desire to be led to your glory. I thank You, God, Creator, because You have blessed me with the joy of your creation; I rejoice in the works of your hands. I have used the mental talents You have given me and I have now completed the work to which You have called me. I have revealed the glory of your works to those who will read my explanations, at least that part of your infinite riches which my limited mind could grasp."

3. Worship the creature or the Creator? In pagan cultures the sun and other celestial bodies are regarded as gods[14].

---

14 **Pagan or heathen:** Christians regard non-Christian peoples who do not know the God of the Bible, as heathens. The corresponding term in the Old Testament is "gentile", which includes all non-Israelites (or non-Jews). It is

The idolatrous worship of heavenly objects, especially the sun, is often the nucleus of pagan religions. The ancient Egyptians honoured the sun-god Ra, and a special temple in Heliopolis (north-east of Cairo) was devoted to him. Right up to 1945 the Japanese shintoists regarded Amaterasu as the supreme sun-god and that the emperor was a descendant of his. The Greek word helios was used for both the sun and the sun-god, whom the Romans worshipped as Sol. The five planets that can be seen with the naked eye, were named after certain gods, according to the then current cult:

- **Mercury:** Mercurius, the Roman god of trade, replaced the Greek god Hermes (protector of thieves and merchants).

- **Venus: the Roman equivalent of the Greek Aphrodite.**

- **Mars: the Roman god of war; Greek: Ares.**

- **Jupiter** was regarded by the Romans as the father of all the gods; the Greeks called him *Zeus*. Both names derive from the same root.

- **Saturn:** the ancient Roman god of agriculture; Greek: *Kronos*.

Even the planets discovered in recent times were given names taken from Greek mythology: **Uranus** (1781), **Neptune** (1846), and **Pluto** (1930).

The Bible very clearly distinguishes between Creator and creature. All created objects, including all the stars, were made by God for certain purposes and functions, and all of them point unmistakably to the existence, the glory, the power and the divinity of the Creator, according to

---

God's will that all peoples should praise Him, including pagans: "Praise the LORD, all you nations; extol Him all you peoples" (Ps 117:1). The Gospel of Jesus Christ is to be proclaimed to all peoples on earth (Matt 28:18-20).

Romans 1:19-20. He alone is worthy of praise and worship. According to the Bible the stars and the planets have no mythological meaning. Their worship is described as idolatry: "If a man or woman living among you … is found doing evil in the eyes of the LORD your God in violation of his covenant, and contrary to my command has worshipped other gods, bowing down to them or to the sun or to the moon or the stars of the sky, … take the man or woman who has done this evil deed to your city gate and stone that person to death" (Deut 17:2-5). Also in the Ten Commandments any kind of stellar cult is explicitly forbidden: "You shall not bow down to them or worship them" (Ex 20:5). A similar admonition is found in Deuteronomy 4:19: "And when you look up to the sky and see the sun, the moon and the stars – all the heavenly array – do not be enticed into bowing down to them and worshipping things …" When Paul came to Athens, he found an altar bearing the inscription: "TO AN UNKNOWN GOD" (Acts 17:23). As mentioned previously, the Greeks had many gods, but they did not know the One true God Who made heaven and earth. They tried to honour Him by building this altar. Using this lack of knowledge as an opening, Paul proclaimed to them "The God who made the world and everything in it is the Lord of heaven and earth" (Acts 17:24). He emphasises that we are not dealing with a distant godlike being who lives beyond the stars (*Schiller*), but that this God is personally interested in our lives. He calls upon us to turn away from our previous ways and He offers us salvation through faith in Jesus Christ:

"In the past God overlooked such ignorance, but now He commands all people everywhere to repent (to change radically). For He has set a day when He will judge the world with justice by the Man (Jesus) He has appointed. He has given proof of this to all men by raising Him from the dead"

(Acts 17:30-31).

8.2 The Stars Proclaim the Glory of God

We read in Psalm 19:1: "The heavens declare the *glory* of God; the skies proclaim the work of his hands." The Hebrew word *kabod* as well as the Greek word *doxa* both mean glory and honour. God's glory is a central theme of the Bible. It refers to the beauty, the majesty, and the heavenly brilliance and splendour of the light emanating from God's nearness. Psalm 150 is a doxology to the glory of God: "Praise God in his sanctuary; praise Him in his mighty heavens. Praise Him for his acts of power; praise Him for his surpassing greatness" (verses 1 & 2). The stars also participate in this praise. If we were to rephrase Psalm 148 in present-day terms, it could read as follows:

Praise the Lord all you galaxies, appearing like
mere dust motes on photographic plates.
Praise the Lord, Sirius and your companions
Arcturus, Aldebaran and Antares.
Praise the Lord, all you meteorites, all you comets
and planets in your elliptical orbits.
Praise the Lord, atmosphere and stratosphere,
X-rays and radio waves.
Praise the Lord, all you atoms and molecules,
protons and electrons, protozoa and radiolaria.
Praise the Lord, all you birds and dragon-flies,
rushing by in the sky.
Praise the Lord, all you microscopic hexagonal
snow crystals; all you lustrous blue prisms of
copper sulphate.
Praise the Lord, all you phosphorescent algae,
anurida maritima and ligia exotica, floating like
sparkling diamonds on the surf.
Praise the Lord, tropic of Cancer, Arctic circle; all
you storms sweeping across the Atlantic Ocean
and along the Humboldt current.
Praise the Lord, dark forests of the Amazon, all

you tropical islands with your volcanoes, and you,
O moon, shining on the swaying palms surround-
ing the lagoon.
Praise the Lord, all you public servants, all you
students, all you young maidens.
Let them praise the name of the Lord, for his
name alone
is exalted; his splendour is above the earth and the
heavens.
He has raised the fortunes of his people and taken
Israel to his heart.
Praise the Lord!

8.3   The Stars as Signs

Let us read verse 14 of the creation account once more:
"Let there be lights in the expanse of the sky to separate
the day from the night, and let them serve as SIGNS to
mark seasons and days and years." It is clear that one of
the tasks assigned by God to astronomical bodies, is to be
signs. The Hebrew word *oth* used here is the same as the
sign God gave Cain: "Then the LORD put a mark on Cain
so that no one who found him would kill him" (Gen 4:15).
When God made a covenant with Noah, He gave the rainbow a meaning so that it would serve as a sign: "I have set
my rainbow in the clouds, and it will be the sign of the
covenant between me and the earth" (Gen 9:13). The word
oth is also used for example in Exodus 7:3: "… though I
multiply my miraculous *signs* and wonders in Egypt."

We may now conclude that the stars not only indicate the
seasons, but they also transmit information pertaining to
their function as signs. An essential characteristic of a sign
is that it points away from itself to something else or to
somebody. The word "sign" can appear in several combi-
nations, like resign, sign on, signature, significance, letter
signs, signals, signs of the times, etc. A sign always has an

assigned meaning. A sign is the simplest form of representation of a person, an object, or an event. In [G6, p 145] the author discusses this basic property of information more fully.

As far as biblical signs are concerned, God defined the codes being used, and explained their meaning. A rainbow, which may be described in terms of the prismatic effects of water droplets in the air, is much more than a mere physical phenomenon. Although white sunlight is optically broken up into the seven visible colours red, orange, yellow, green, blue, indigo, and violet, God ordained that this natural occurrence should be the sign of a covenant:

> "Whenever I bring clouds over the earth and the rainbow appears in the clouds, I will remember my covenant between me and you and all living creatures of every kind. Never again will the waters become a flood to destroy all life" (Gen 9:14-15).

As is customary in informatics, any agreed-on sign must have a unique meaning, whether it refers to a phenomenon, an event, or an object. Once this has been determined, the code does not change. The Bible contains many further examples of the way God assigned unique meanings to various symbols. Certain objects or prescribed actions[15] had specific meanings. The brazen serpent, which was a sign of healing from the venomous snakes in the desert, was also a sign pointing to the crucified Saviour (compare Numbers 21:6-9 and John 3:14-15). In

---

15 **Significant acts:** The circumcision of male infants on the eighth day was a sign of the covenant God made with Abraham (Gen 17:9-12). The blood smeared on the door frames of the Israelites' houses in Egypt (Exodus 12:7 & 12-13), was a sign of recognition for the angel of death, and it pointed to the perfect Passover lamb – Christ! According to 1 Corinthians 11:24-25 holy communion is celebrated in remembrance of Christ's death, as a symbol of our salvation through his death. Personal belief in the Lord Jesus Christ, and baptism in faith, is a sign of the covenant; of the fact that we are children of God.

what follows, we will restrict ourselves to topics related to the theme of this book – the signs assigned to the stars.

8.3.1 The Constellations

We read in Job 38:32: "Can you bring forth the constellations in their seasons?" It is significant that the Bible (indirectly) refers to the signs of the zodiac, those → constellations used in the setting up of horoscopes. Such fortune-telling and augury is condemned by God in Deuteronomy 18:10-13: "Let no one be found among you … who practises divination or sorcery, interprets omens, engages in witchcraft, or casts spells, or who is a medium or spiritist or who consults the dead. Anyone who does these things is detestable to the LORD … You must be blameless before the LORD your God." In Isaiah 47:13-14 we also find an emphatic condemnation of augury in men's lives. Those who practise such things, will be judged by God:

> "Let your astrologers come forward, those stargazers who make predictions month by month, let them save you from what is coming upon you. Surely they are like stubble; the fire will burn them up. They cannot save themselves from the power of the flame."

When Josiah became king of Judah, the sun, the moon and the stars were worshipped in both Israel and Judah. Josiah put an end to this abominable cult: "He did away with the pagan priests … – those who burned incense to Baal, to the sun and moon, to the constellations and to all the starry hosts" (2 Kings 23:5).

Similar grave warnings are found in Leviticus 20:6: "I will set my face against the person who turns to mediums and spiritists to prostitute himself by following them, and I will cut him off from his people." The New Testament very explicitly excludes idolaters and sorcerers from eternal life: "– their place will be in the fiery lake of burning sulphur" (Rev 21:8). Why does God forbid this kind of divination when He Himself made the stars and confirmed that they would serve as signs? According to Psalm 19 the stars should also glorify God.

The stars were made by God and carry His message. It is thus natural for the arch deceiver to try to distort the actual information and misuse it for his purposes. This forgery and misuse is apparent in astrology[16], which is an anti-biblical practice. All activities where the signs of the zodiac or any other constellations are given astrological meanings, are contrary to the will of God. He abhors it when we occupy ourselves with such things. Today there is hardly any newspaper which does not print horoscopes and other untruthful information. The devil is interested in such false publicity and welcomes it as serving his cause. According to astrological theories not all stars affect our lives, but only the planets, the sun, the moon and the stars of the zodiac. It is rather surprising then that well-known constellations like the Great Bear and the host of more than one (or two) hundred thousand million stars of the Milky Way, all of which radiate their own light, are astrologically "inactive". Astrology is an inheritance from pagan religions where the planets and the constellations of the zodiac were seen as gods who influenced historical events on earth either benignly or maliciously.

We do not know whether the signs of the zodiac were originally given meanings by God, but we should not exclude such a possibility. If it were the case, then should

---

16 **Astrology:** The prefix *astro* is derived from the Greek word *aster* which means star, and the Greek word *logos* means doctrine, reason, or word. The word *astrology* could have had a special meaning, namely for the study of celestial bodies and their biblical meaning and origin. Unfortunately this highly suitable word is now used for activities which God has strictly forbidden, namely fortune-telling based on the stars.

it not be our task to research these original messages? Let us now discuss the possible original meanings of the signs of the zodiac. Three basic aspects have to be considered:

1. Since the earliest historical times the signs (see footnote 43 within chapter A3) of the zodiac were recognised similarly by various nations. It is significant that all but one of them (Libra, the Scales) were given the names of living beings, even though these might differ. This was the case for the early Babylonians and also for the ancient Egyptian and Chinese kingdoms.

2. The stars and the constellations were created by God. And they are good, as stated in 1 Timothy 4:4: "For everything God created is good." This includes the entire original creation and the stars and their message.

3. The message God assigned to the stars must be equivalent to that which we find in the Bible. In this context Paul writes: "It is no trouble for me to write the same things to you again, and it is a safeguard for you" (Phil 3:1).

We have the complete written Word of God which comprises an absolutely trustworthy guide for faith and for life. This was not always the case. During the first third of mankind's history – from Adam to Abraham – probably only a few written notes were available, describing the chief characters mentioned in Genesis chapters 5, 10, and 11. It is therefore plausible that the signs placed in the heavens by God, proclaiming his glory, were originally given as a visual aid to mankind. Let us now pursue the idea that God is telling us something by means of the stars in the zodiac, something more than that which is written in the creation account. This message must agree with the main themes of the Bible.

The Gospel of Jesus already begins in Genesis 3:15 with the words "And I will put enmity between you and the woman, and between your offspring and hers; he (Jesus) will crush your head, and you will strike his heel." Given this biblical background, it is possible that God had already enshrined this information in the signs of the zodiac. Being indelibly written in the sky, such a message would even survive the holocaust of the flood and the confusion of tongues at Babel. It is not possible to trace the original meanings of the signs of the zodiac, but we may try to infer these in the light of the full Gospel message available to us. We have a case of information transfer when God expresses fundamental messages by means of the signs embedded in the constellations. If God has expressed a central message via constellations and man interprets these, then it involves a process of information transfer. We may therefore apply the five levels of information transfer [G8, p 138-141] here:

1. The statistical level (the statistical aspect of the signs which are used): The points of light observed in the night sky transmit the intended signals. This is an application of the statement in the creation account that the stars would serve as signs (Gen 1:14).

2. Syntax (the combination of signs): The sun passes through the thirteen signs of the zodiac on the ecliptic as seen from the earth. If we presume that these constellations comprise a code, then we may conclude that there are thirteen[17] divine messages.

3. The semantic aspect (the meaningfullnes of information): We will now assign biblical truths to the well-known international (Latin) names of the zodiac constellations. It should be emphasised that we are now devising a freely structured conceptual model – we are definitely not involved in actual scriptural exegesis. Our purpose is

---

17 Astrology assumes that there are 12 signs of the zodiac. In reality, the sun passes through 13 constellations in a year. Between Sagittarius and Scorpio we find the constellation Ophiucus (see also Footnote 43).

to provide a visual aid to remind us of salient biblical affirmations when we see the zodiac constellations or hear their names. The following biblical meanings are fairly open-ended, but we have tried to associate suitable scriptural truths with each constellation. We could also formulate our objective as follows: **The celestial billboard belongs to God!** Both the Latin and the common names of the stars are given.

1. *Capricorn, the Goat:* "The high mountains belong to the wild goats; the crags are a refuge for the coneys (rock badgers or hyrax)" (Ps 104:18). This verse expresses God's care for his creation. In Matthew 10:29-31 Jesus also emphasises this: "Are not two sparrows sold for a penny? Yet not one of them will fall to the ground apart from the will of your Father... So don't be afraid; you are worth more than many sparrows." In the sermon on the mount Jesus gives another illustration of God's care: "If that is how God clothes the grass of the field, which is here today and tomorrow is thrown into the fire, will He not much more clothe you, O you of little faith?" (Matt 6:30). God's loving care includes the grass, the sparrows, and the goats; how much more would it not then include human beings! We read in Philippians 4:6: "Do not be anxious about anything, but in everything, by prayer and petition, with thanksgiving, present your requests to God."

2. *Aquarius, the Water Bearer:* The flood in the time of Noah was an extraordinary world-wide event. Everybody was destroyed by the floodwaters, except those who belonged to God. The people who did not know God did not expect this judgment. In Matthew 24 Jesus discusses his second coming, and He compares the future situation with that in the time of Noah:

"As it was in the days of Noah, so it will be at the coming of the Son of Man. For in the days before the flood, people were eating and drinking, marrying and giving in marriage, up to the day Noah entered the ark; and they knew nothing about what would happen until the flood came and took them all away. That is how it will be at the coming of the Son of Man. Two men will be in the field; one will be taken and the other left. Two women will be grinding with a hand mill; one will be taken and the other left" (Matt 24:37-41).

3. *Pisces, the Fishes:* "Come, follow me, ... and I will make you fishers of men" (Matt 4:19). It is Jesus's intention that this good news – the gospel of salvation – the best news ever given to mankind, should be proclaimed and spread. All the world must hear his Word: "Therefore go and make disciples of all nations, ... teaching them to obey everything I have commanded you" (Matt 28:19-20). Our assignment is to win people for Jesus. He compares this ministry with fishing. For the first Christians the fish also had another meaning. They used a fish as a symbol referring to Jesus and to express their kinship to Him. The Greek word for fish is ICHTHYS, and this is an acronym[18] for the Greek phrase Iesous CHristos THeou Yios Soter (Jesus Christ, Son of God, Saviour).

4. *Aries, the Ram:* "Abraham ... took the ram and sacrificed it ... instead of his son" (Gen 22:13). God tested Abraham's faith to see whether he would be prepared to sacrifice his only son, Isaac. After Abraham had agreed and had prepared everything for the sacrifice, an angel of the Lord restrained him. Instead of his son he then sacrificed a ram. This ram illustrates God's way of grace: "He who did not spare his own Son, but gave Him up for us all – how will He not also, along with Him, graciously give us all things?" (Rom 8:32).

---

18 **Acronym** (Greek *ákros* = summit, extreme end; *ónyma* = name): It is an abbreviation consisting of the first letters of some words. This new word often has a special meaning, e. g. NATO, UNESCO.

5. Taurus, the Bull: There are many prophetic pronouncements in the Old Testament about the coming Saviour, the Messiah. Psalm 22 is one of them. Jesus's suffering on the cross is described in detail. Even his last loud cry (Matt 27: 46; Mark 15:34) appears in this Psalm: "My God, my God, why have You forsaken Me?" (Ps 22:1). The raging, scoffing crowd around Him is prophetically compared with strong fighting bulls: "Many bulls surround me; strong bulls of Bashan encircle me. Roaring lions tearing their prey open their mouths wide against me" (Ps 22:12-13). The bull in the zodiac could therefore proclaim Christ's suffering. In addition to the pain and suffering, He was also afflicted by the scorn, the hate, the resentment, and the rebellion of the inflamed crowd. In Isaiah 43:24 God says: "you have burdened Me with your sins and wearied Me with your offences."

6. Gemini, the Twins: One of the fundamental messages of the Bible is that one must repent to be saved: "Repent and live!" (Ezek 18:32). Jesus also teaches that nobody will enter the kingdom of God unless he repents: "I tell you the truth, unless you change and become like little children, you will never enter the kingdom of heaven" (Matt 18:3). Repentance is clearly an essential event in the course of one's life. If you neglect this, you stand judged and will be eternally doomed. The other side of the coin of repentance is to be born again – these two are twins. During the pertinent conversation in the night with Nicodemus, a learned Jew, Jesus told him: "unless a man is born again, he cannot see the kingdom of God" (John 3:3). This may create the impression that one more act is required for entry into heaven. But, in fact, the two events cannot be separated. When a sinner repents, God's response is to cause him or her be born again. Repentance and the event of being born again, are two sides of the same coin; they are the twins of our salvation.

7. Cancer, the Crab: Some of the more distressful aspects of human society include slander and idle gossip. In 2 Timothy 2:16-17 Paul warns us in the following words: "Avoid godless chatter because those who indulge in it will become more and more ungodly. Their teaching will spread like gangrene." (In other translations and in other languages "cancer" is used instead of "gangrene". The original Greek word refers to something which consumes the body from within.)

"The tongue is a small part of the body, but it makes great boasts. Consider what a great forest is set on fire by a small spark" (James 3:5). Man can tame huge animals, "but no man can tame the tongue. It is a restless evil, full of deadly poison" (James 3:8).

Jesus tells us to be careful with our words: "I tell you that men will have to give account on the day of judgment for every careless word they have spoken" (Matt 12:36). The existence of a repository in which all our evil, indifferent, superfluous and self-extolling words are stored, should gravely concern us. It would appal us, but we could still call on the pardoning, cleansing grace of the Lord Jesus Christ. The cancer of sin is consuming us from within and we can only find purification and deliverance through Christ.

8. Leo, the Lion: Jesus is the Lion of the tribe of Judah. His first coming is prophesied in Genesis 49:9-10: "You are a lion's cub, O Judah … The sceptre will not depart from Judah, nor the ruler's staff from between his feet, until he comes to whom it belongs and the obedience of the nations is his". We are told in Revelation 5 that the Lion of Judah and the Lamb of God is one and the same person, namely Jesus:

"See, the Lion of the tribe of Judah, the Root of David, has triumphed. He is able to open the scroll and its seven seals" (Rev 5:5).

"... because you were slain and with your blood you purchased men for God from every tribe and language and people and nation... Worthy is the Lamb, who was slain, to receive power and wealth and wisdom and strength and honour and glory and praise!" (Rev 5:9 & 12).

9. *Virgo, the Virgin:* Jesus, the Son of God, entered this world as a human being. His coming is first mentioned in Genesis 3:15: "And I will put enmity between you and the woman, and between your offspring and hers." He would be born of a virgin (Luke 1:27) and comes to us as a man: "The Word became flesh and lived for a while among us. We have seen his glory, the glory of the one and only Son, who came from the Father, full of grace and truth" (John 1:14). He left the splendour of heaven to come down to the earth to save us: "(He) made himself nothing, taking the very nature of a servant, being made in human likeness. And being found in appearance as a man ..." (Phil 2:7).

10. *Libra, the Scales:* God weighed the Babylonian king Belshazzar[19] according to Daniel 5. God's judgment appeared in the form of secret writing on the wall: "Mene, mene, tekel, parsin" (Dan 5:25). Only Daniel could explain these words, having received a revelation from God:

> "This is what these words mean: *Mene:* God has numbered the days of your reign and brought it

---

19 **Belshazzar:** He was the eldest son of *Nabonid*, the last king of the Chaldean kingdom. When *Nabonid* was in Arabia (the north-western part, 552 – 542 B.C.), *Belshazzar* reigned in Babylon as his regent. As regent he was known as the son of *Nebuchadnezzar* (Daniel 5:18,22), the king of Babylon (Dan 7:1), the king of the Chaldeans (Dan 5:30), or simply as "the king" (Dan 5:1). *Belshazzar's* blasphemy was that he used the holy utensils from the Temple of Jerusalem for such a mundane purpose as a drunken revelry. He was murdered that same night when Daniel explained the meaning of the secret writing. *Darius*, the Mede, then conquered his kingdom.

to an end. *Tekel:* You have been weighed on the scales and found wanting. *Peres:* Your kingdom is divided and given to the Medes and Persians"

(Dan 5:26-28).

Like Belshazzar, all people will be judged by God: "For He has set a day when He will judge the world with justice by the man He has appointed" (Acts 17:31). This man is named in 2 Corinthians 5:10: "For we must all appear before the judgment seat of Christ, that each one may receive what is due to him for the things done while in the body, whether good or bad."

11. *Scorpio, the Scorpion:* Jesus had to die so that we could be saved, and through his death He has triumphed over eternal death. The first gospel message of the Bible (the proto gospel) is spelled out as follows: "He will crush your head, and you will strike his heel" (Gen 3:15). God's enemy was defeated on the cross; the price was Jesus's death. Death was the sting of the enemy, the deadly scorpion. "But God raised Him from the dead, freeing Him from the agony of death" (Acts 2:24). The victory over hell, death, and the devil was gained:

"Where, O death, is your victory?"
"Where, O death, is your sting?" (1 Cor 15:55).

12. *Ophiucus, the Serpent-Bearer:* In the garden of Eden, the serpent tempted Eve to eat the fruit which God had forbidden. Thus sin entered the world with the consequence that humanity was separated from God. Centuries later, as the people of Israel wandered through the Wilderness for forty years, a precarious incident occurred. Poisonous snakes appeared and the people died from the snake bites. Moses asked God for help and received an unusual command: "Make a snake and put it on a pole; anyone who is bitten can look at it and live" (Num 4:8). So Moses became a serpent-bearer. If someone was bitten and looked at the snake, then he would live. Some thought this foolish and

thought that they could spare themselves the trouble of looking at the snake. However, because they did not believe in the way of salvation God provided, these people died. In the New Testament Jesus uses this incident to explain how salvation would be won through his work on the cross: "Just as Moses lifted up the snake in the desert, so the Son of man must be lifted up, that everyone who believes in him may have eternal life" (John 3:14-15). Only the person who puts their faith in Jesus receives eternal life. All others will be lost for ever.

13. *Sagittarius, the Archer:* Apart from God we miss our purpose. Death is the result of sin (Rom 6:23). The Greek word for sin is *hamartia*, which was derived from the sport of archery. The archer expects his arrows to hit the target. When he misses, it is called *hamartia*. Our natural inclination is to exclude God from our lives. Sin causes this tragic separation, but anybody can take the necessary steps towards salvation during the course of his life: "Repent, then, and turn to God, so that your sins may be wiped out" (Acts 3:19).

4. The pragmatic aspect (the behavioural aspect): After we have taken note of the above mentioned biblical truths, we should consider our response. The jailer of Philippi found himself in a similar situation when he had heard the message of the Gospel: "what must I do to be saved?" (Acts 16:30). He received the concise but definite answer from Paul and Silas: "Believe in the Lord Jesus, and you will be saved – you and your household" (Acts 16:31). He accepted this and let himself be baptised immediately. That was an active pragmatic response! The same type of response is expected of us.

5. The apobetic aspect (purposefulness; the deductive aspect): This is the highest level of transfer of information. The question is whether the sender achieves his intended purpose with the recipient. God is the Sender and we are the recipients of his message. We fulfil the purpose when we accept the Gospel. Everybody who accepts Jesus Christ, is saved: "whoever hears my word and believes Him Who sent Me has eternal life and will not be condemned; he has crossed over from death to life" (John 5:24). He who has found Jesus, has eternal life; he has achieved the intended purpose.

8.3.2 The Darkness on Calvary

Of all the stars the sun is the most important one for us. As recorded in the Bible, signs occurred in the sun only in highly exceptional cases. When Christ was crucified, the brightness of day was replaced by darkness. Luke describes this event as follows:

> "And it was about the sixth hour[20], and there was a darkness over all the earth until the ninth hour. And the sun, was darkened …"
>
> (Luke 23:44-45 KJV).

The parallel accounts in Matthew 27:45 and Mark 15:33 are similar, but the sun is not mentioned. It may seem that a total eclipse of the sun might have caused this darkness. When the sun is eclipsed, its brightness is decreased by a factor of 1600 million. It then becomes so dark that many stars are visible. But the sun can only be eclipsed when the moon is in its dark phase and passes between the sun and the earth. The moon's orbit makes an angle of 5° 8' 43" with the plane of the ecliptic. This means that there are only two points of intersection, and an eclipse can only occur when the moon is exactly in the plane of the earth's

---

20 In New Testament times both day and night were divided into 12 hours each. The length of these hours varied, depending on the time from sunrise to sunset. But the end of the sixth hour always coincided with noon. The night was divided into four watches of three hours each: evening, midnight, cock-crow, and morning.

orbit, i. e. at one of the two points of intersection. We may therefore reject the possibility of an eclipse on the following grounds:

(a) *Time:* Jesus was crucified at the time of the Passover, celebrated by the Jews when the moon was full at the beginning of the northern spring season, on the fourteenth day of the month Nisan[21]. (The Christian Easter, when we celebrate the resurrection of Jesus, occurs on the first Sunday after the spring full moon, as decided by the Council of Nicea in the year 325). The darkness which accompanied the crucifixion, could not have been caused by an eclipse of the sun, because the moon was exactly at the opposite side of its orbit.

(b) *Duration:* Because of the relative motions of the moon and the earth, and the rotation of the earth, the shadow of the moon travels at a speed of 28 km/min on the surface of the earth at the equator. The maximum possible duration of a total eclipse of the sun is eight minutes. But the darkness described in the crucifixion account lasted a full three hours, from the sixth to the ninth hour, i. e. from noon until 3.00 p. m. This immediately excludes an eclipse as the cause of the darkness.

We conclude: God Himself must have intervened. He is the Lord of everything. "Darkness came over all the land" (Matt 27:45). This darkness is a definite, unmistakable sign, given three times in the New Testament in extra-

---

21 **The month Nisan** (Nehemiah 2:1), previously known as Abib (Ex 13:4), was taken as the first month of the year by God (Ex 12:2-3) to remind the Israelites of their exodus from Egypt. It lasted from the middle of March to the middle of April. Their year was based on the phases of the moon, and the first day of each month was a new moon festival. The Passover was celebrated on the 14th of Nisan (Ex 12:18, Lev 23:5). This was followed by the week-long festival of unleavened bread (Lev 23:6), from the 15th to the 21st day of Nisan. According to John 19:14 Jesus died on the day of preparation before the Passover week – i. e. the 14th of Nisan.

ordinary circumstances, namely when Christ died (Matt 27:35 & 45), shortly before his second coming (Matt 24:29), and when the sixth seal is opened (Rev 6:12). In all three cases astronomical explanations are inadequate.

The concept of darkness while the sun is still shining appears to be upheld by Exodus 10:22-23, where the Egyptians experienced a plague of darkness while at the same time the Israelites had "light in the places where they lived", i. e. in the land of Goshen. However, no explanation for this is given in the biblical text other than it was a miracle wrought by God.

The concept of God miraculously using a cloud to shut out light is seen in Exodus 14:19-20, where there was a pillar of cloud between the fleeing Israelites and the pursuing Egyptians. This cloud was sufficiently luminous on the Israelite side to give light to up 2 million people (cf. the intensity of say the light pylons of several football fields), but the cloud prevented this light from shining through so that it was dark on the Egyptian side.

What did God want to tell the people then, and to us now, through this darkening of the sun? A fundamental problem of exegesis to consider now, is whether biblical affirmations are always unique, or can have various meanings. Whenever the Bible answers a question, it is always unambiguous. Jesus gave definite answers to all questions. On the question of salvation He emphasises that there is only one way which leads to the Father: "I am the way and the truth and the life. No one comes to the Father except through me" (John 14:6). There is only one gate leading to heaven; all other religions are deplorable human delusions (discussed fully in [G7]).

When we attach meanings to biblical pronouncements and illustrations, these meanings should be consistent with the central message of the Bible, and also agree with other biblical relationships. First of all, lets us note that this darkness was a sign given by God. In Scripture darkness and night often are signs of disaster and horror (Ps 107:10, Jer 13:16), judgment, and separation from God (Matt 8:12, John 1:5). We may now assign four meanings to the darkness at the time of the crucifixion:

1. Judgment of the Jews: Being "the light of the world" (John 8:12), Jesus warned the people against the darkness awaiting those who do not believe in Him: "You are going to have the light just a little while longer. Walk while you have the light, before darkness overtakes you. The man who walks in the dark does not know where he is going. Put your trust in the light while you have it, so that you may become sons of light" (John 12:35-36). In Matthew 23: 37-38 Jesus took note of their choice and its consequences: "...but you were not willing. Look, your house is left to you desolate." Anybody who rejects Jesus, remains unsaved. In the Bible this state of being lost is always compared to darkness (e. g. Matt 8:12, Matt 22:13, Col 1:13, Jude:6). It is explicitly stated that the entire nation falls under this darkness (Matt 27:45). It is therefore clear that the Jewish nation would be overtaken by the spiritual darkness against which Jesus had warned so strongly in John 12:35-36. The Jews are still struck by this blindness which prevents them from accepting Jesus as their Messiah and Saviour. Paul writes in Romans 9:27: "Though the number of the Israelites be like the sand by the sea, only the remnant will be saved." There is a parallel for this New Testament darkness in the Old Testament. Because of Pharaoh's hardened heart, Egypt was struck with darkness for three days (the ninth plague): "So Moses stretched out his hand towards the sky, and total darkness covered all Egypt for three days ... Yet all the Israelites had light in the places where they lived" (Ex 10:22-23). Pharaoh was confronted by Moses on several occasions with the living God, but he rejected Him.

Then followed the judgment of the hardening of Pharaoh's heart; the *three-day* darkness was the sign. At that time Israel was excepted because they believed God's message. But when God sent them the Messiah, they rejected Him, and then their hearts were hardened. Up to the present time "a veil covers their hearts" (2 Cor 3:15). The *three-hour* darkness of the crucifixion was a sign of their obduracy. The occurrence of the number *three* in both instances is noteworthy.

2. Judgment of sin: God's judgment of sin was enacted on Calvary. The Lord Jesus came as "the Lamb of God, who takes away the sin of the world" (John 1:29). The purpose of His incarnation was to bear the burden of our sins in our place. On Calvary the entire fury of God's wrath against sin was poured out on Jesus. God turned his back on Christ, who then had to suffer the judgment which should have struck us because of our sins. He suffered the agony of being forsaken by God, which nobody else had ever experienced. The severe darkness was a sign expressing this separation, and towards the end of this dark period (the ninth hour) Jesus cried out: "My God, my God, why have You forsaken Me?" (Matt 27:46).

3. A sign of an extraordinary event: When God does something out of the ordinary which is also something unique, then such an act is often accompanied by signs. The water which was turned into wine at the wedding in Cana was the sign indicating the beginning of Jesus's ministry on earth. And his crucifixion is of fundamental importance for our salvation. It was a unique sacrifice for the salvation of mankind: "because by one sacrifice He has made perfect for ever those who are being made holy" (Hebr 10:14). The darkness at the time of the crucifixion emphasises the magnitude of this event. The only person who really understood the significance of this sign, was the heathen Roman centurion "who stood there in front of

Jesus ... (and) said: 'Surely this man was the Son of God!' " (Mark 15:39). Every Jew could observe that something very extraordinary had occurred, but their observation did not result in a profession of faith.

4. It was not just the sun which became dim: In the last chapter of the Old Testament the Lord Jesus is called "the sun of righteousness": "But for you who revere my name, the sun of righteousness will rise with healing in its wings" (Malachi 4:2). In biblical symbolism He is "the sun who smiles down on me". But on the cross He lost his brilliance. In Isaiah 53:2 Jesus is described as having "no beauty or majesty to attract us to him." When He died on the cross with the exclamation: "Father, into your hands I commit my spirit" (Luke 23:46), He lost his brilliance, just like the sun. He predicted that "the Son of Man will be *three* days and *three* nights in the heart of the earth" (Matt 12:40), and as an appropriate sign, the sun was dark for *three* hours. The sun that we see in the sky, will eventually cease to exist; its brilliance is meant for this creation only. In the new creation prepared by God, there will be another source of light, eternally: "The city does not need the sun or the moon to shine on it, for the glory of God gives it light, and the Lamb (Jesus) is its lamp" (Rev 21:23).

8.3.3 The Southern Cross

Of all the constellations the Southern Cross (Latin *Crux*) is probably the easiest to recognise. Although it is the smallest constellation (measuring only 68.5 square degrees out of a total sky area of 41,253 square degrees), it is the most conspicuous and therefore the best-known constellation in the southern skies (see *Figure 4*). The four main stars are distinguished by Greek letters, as is customary for all constellations. Their distances and apparent magnitudes are as follows:

Alpha Crucis	370 light-years, magnitude 0.8
	(It is a quadruple star; one of the four is 3,000 times as bright as the sun, and another one 1,900 times.)
Beta Crucis	500 light-years, magnitude 1.3
	(It is 6,000 times as bright as the sun.)
Gamma Crucis	88 light-years, magnitude 1.6
	(120 times as bright as the sun)
Delta Crucis	260 light-years, magnitude 2.8
	(370 times as bright as the sun)

The Southern Cross encompasses an area rich in bright stars. The density of stars of magnitude 5 and brighter is 19.12 stars per square degree. In contrast, the constellation known as the *Sextant*, has a density of only 0.63 stars per square degree.

Celestial Pole: If one extends the long axis of the Southern Cross (from Gamma Crucis to Alpha Crucis, also known as Acrux) 4.5 times, the approximate position of the southern celestial pole can be determined. In the northern hemisphere the *Pole Star* indicates the position of the northern celestial pole, but there is no such (visible) star in the south indicating the point around which the stars rotate. The celestial poles enable us to find the true north-south direction, but we can also determine the exact latitude of our position on earth. It is only necessary to measure the angle between the horizon and the celestial pole.

The southern and northern celestial poles are imaginary points around which the entire celestial sphere seems to rotate. The earth's axis of rotation extends through these points and all the stars seem to rotate around the celestial poles. This effect is the result of the rotation of the earth, whereas the stars are "fixed". When you are at the North Pole, the Pole Star is vertically above you; similarly for an observer at the South Pole the southern celestial pole is precisely overhead. When one moves away from either pole, the celestial pole goes down towards the horizon. The earth's axis of rotation passes through both poles, and the stars seem to rotate in the opposite direction.

View from the poles: When you look straight up from the North Pole, you will see the northern celestial pole and all the stars will appear to rotate anti-clockwise around that point. On the other hand, at the South Pole the stars seem to rotate in a clockwise direction. At a pole the apparent courses of the stars are circles which are parallel to the

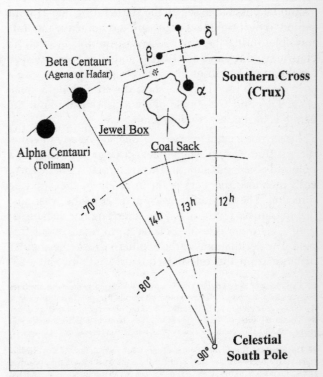

Figure 4: *The Southern Cross and the two Pointers, Beta Centauri (Agena) and Alpha Centauri (Toliman).*

horizon. Both the sun and the stars seem to move in this peculiar fashion. And all the stars visible at one time are always visible; they do not rise or set. But one can only see one half of the celestial sphere.

View from the equator: At the equator the earth's axis, including its celestial extension, lies in the plane of the horizon[22]. No star seems to rotate around a pole, but all stars rise and set. The Pole Star lies exactly on the horizon, and the southern celestial pole also. It is only possible at the equator to see all stars during the course of one year. (It would be possible to see all the stars during one 24 hour period, if the brightness of the sun did not make the stars invisible during the day.) As seen from the equator, all stars move through a semi-circle, and all of them are seen for the same length of time every night. Stars close to a pole seem to travel only a short distance along a small semicircle, and the course of stars passing through the zenith is the largest possible semi-circle.

The view from a latitude between 0° and 90°: At any intermediate latitude φ some stars follow circular paths around a pole and others rise and set. The earth rotates from west to east; therefore the stars seem to rotate in the opposite direction. They rise in the east and set in the west, just like the sun and the moon. Stars at an angular distance of $\pm 90° - \varphi$ from a celestial pole, seem to rotate about that pole. The declination[23] of the Southern Cross (the angular distance from the celestial equator[24]) is between $-63°$

---

22 **The plane of the horizon:** This is a plane which meets the earth's surface tangentially at the point where the observer stands. The point vertically above the observer is known as the zenith. When the observer is located on either the Tropic of Cancer or the Tropic of Capricorn (latitude $\pm 23.5°$), then the sun passes through the zenith once every year, namely on June 21 or December 22.

23 **Declination:** This is the angular distance between a star and the celestial equator; the declination of stars north of the equator is regarded as positive, and south is taken as negative. Declination is a celestial co-ordinate designated by δ. At the celestial north pole $\delta = 90°$, and $\delta = -90°$ at the south pole. The declination of stars on the celestial equator is: $\delta = 0°$.

(Alpha Crucis) and $-56°$ (Gamma Crucis). As seen from Cape Town ($\varphi = -34° =$ latitude 34° south) the entire Southern Cross is always visible above the horizon (see *Figure 5*). At its lowest position Gamma Crucis is in the horizon: $-90° - (-56°) = -34°$. Alpha Crucis is 7° higher.

The Southern Cross is thus circumpolar as seen from Cape Town. At Johannesburg ($\varphi = -27°$) the lower part of its circuit is below the horizon, as shown in *Figure 5*. The apparent courses of all stars as seen from any point on earth, are either complete circles or exact circular arcs.

At the equator all visible stars in both hemispheres can be seen at one time or another, but at the poles only one half of the stars are visible. One can therefore expect to see other stars at other latitudes. The farther away one is from the equator, the fewer stars can be observed. Depending on the latitude φ of the observer, the visible portion of the stars is as follows:

- All stars up to a polar distance[25] $h = \varphi$ are circumpolar.

- Stars having a polar distance h between φ and $180° - \varphi$, rise and set.

- Stars having a polar distance h between $180° - \varphi$ and $180°$,

cannot be observed.

It follows that the part of the sky where an observer at latitude φ sees circumpolar stars, is just as large as the part

---

24 **Celestial equator:** This is an imaginary circle in the sky, perpendicular to the earth's axis. It may be regarded as a projection of the earth's equator, and it is the separating line between the northern and the southern celestial hemispheres.

25 **Polar distance:** The polar distance h of a star is its angular distance from the north celestial pole. It varies from 0° at the north pole to 180° at the south pole.

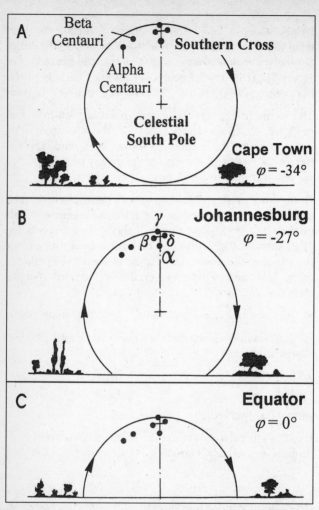

Figure 5: *The various arcs traced by the Southern Cross. At the latitude of Cape Town the arc is a full circle lying above the horizon (A; the stars are circumpolar). In B, as seen from the latitude of Johannesburg, a part of the circle lies below the horizon. C depicts the situation at the equator.*

which he can never see. At latitude φ that segment of the sky around the opposite pole up to an angular distance of φ, can never be observed.

The Jewel Box: Many open star clusters can be seen inside the Southern Cross. The best known is the beautiful *NGC 4755*, also designated *Kappa Crucis*. It is close to Beta Crucis. With the naked eye one can only discern a faint, indistinct star. But binoculars provide a glimpse of the fairest view in the starry skies. Consisting of 50 stars at a distance of 980 light-years, it is a cluster similar to the Pleiades, but considerably lovelier. Nowhere else is there such a magnificent group of glittering stars, shimmering with a profusion of colours, varying from pastel shades of blue, and red, to purple and yellow – a real glittering treasure chest! Astronomer *John Herschel* (1792 – 1871) very aptly called it "The Jewel Box".

The Coal Sack: Included in the area of the Southern Cross there are very many other faint stars also belonging to the Milky Way. Some of them may be seen with the aid of binoculars. But between Alpha and Beta Crucis there is a dark cloud where not a single star can be seen. This cloud seems to consist of relatively dense interstellar matter. These dust particles block out the light of the stars which are behind the cloud, so that it seems to be as dark as a coal sack. This is the best example of a dark cloud which can be seen by the naked eye (more correctly: cannot be seen!).

The Celestial Clock: The Southern Cross can also be used to determine the time of day. This is possible in South Africa (also in Australia, New Zealand and South America) although it must be noted that the Southern Cross is not always visible in the northern hemisphere. You can determine the time in this way: Hold the 24-hour clock-face in *Figure 6* in a vertical position with the present month at the top. If it is the middle of a month, then choose a position halfway between two months. Now hold the disk in such a way that the long axis of the Southern Cross points to its centre. This imaginary line then indicates the time to the nearest hour.

If you look towards the celestial south pole and imagine that there is a 24-hour clock-face, then the position of the Southern Cross changes according to the time and the season. In the middle of February the cross is at its highest point, the 12 o'clock position, at 9 p. m. Two hours earlier it would have been at the 11 o'clock position, and when it is 11 p. m., the cross will be at the 1 o'clock position. When the Southern Cross is at the 12 o'clock position, then two of the brightest stars of the firmament can be seen around 11 o'clock. These two are the famous "Pointers", Alpha and Beta Centauri.

The Pointers: The two bright stars near the Southern Cross are known as the Pointers. The one nearest to the Cross is *Beta Centauri*, also known as *Agena*. It is the eleventh brightest star (apparent magnitude 0.6) in the southern sky and its absolute luminosity is 10,000 times that of the sun. Its distance from earth is 490 light-years. The other one is *Alpha Centauri*, or *Toliman*. It is the third brightest star (apparent magnitude −0.27) as seen from earth[26]. It actually comprises three stars orbiting one another. Only two of these can be seen through binoculars. The third one is so faint that it can only be observed by means of a large telescope. This third member of the triad often comes closest to earth of any "fixed" star; it is therefore also known as *Proxima Centauri* (Latin: *proximus* = the nearest). At its nearest position, its distance from the earth is 4.25 light-years. It is however customary to ignore the

---

26 **Bright stars:** *Sirius* (*Alpha Canis Majoris* in the constellation *Canis Major, The Large Dog*), with an apparent magnitude of −1.46, is the brightest star as seen from earth. The second brightest star is *Canopus* (*Alpha Carinae* in the constellation *The Ship*); its apparent magnitude is −0.72.

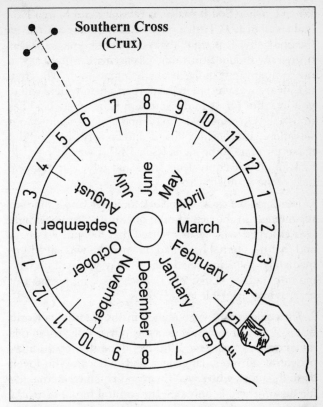

Figure 6: *The Southern Cross as the hour hand of a clock. Hold the disk so that the current month is at the top. In this case June is at the top, and the indicated hour is 6 o'clock (in this case 6.00 p. m.).*

three components and to simply refer to Alpha Centauri as being approximately 4.3 light-years distant. It is then usually stated that the (bright) Alpha Centauri is the nearest star (apart from the sun).

When I visited South Africa in February and March 1992 and again in 1995, I often observed the Southern Cross in the night sky. This sight always fascinated me anew and turned my thoughts inwards. Observing the night sky in my company, one of the local inhabitants said: "The cross of Calvary was erected in the northern hemisphere where you live. But for us in the southern hemisphere God has drawn the cross in the sky to remind us continually of our salvation." I reconsider this idea to be very apt. God did make the stars to be signs (Gen 1:14). I was inspired to look for biblical equivalents and signs in the astronomical facts of the Southern Cross.

1. *The Cross as a clock:* This clock indicates God's time for repentance. In the last minute one of the criminals who was crucified with Jesus realised that the end was near and that the eternal hour had dawned; he was saved immediately. Jesus informed him: "today you will be with me in paradise" (Luke 23:43). Such a saving moment of grace is also available to each of us.

2. *The earth's pivot:* Who stands in the middle of world history? Any of the great generals? Or any of the famous inventors or explorers? Who has done the most for all people of all races, languages and nations? Who loved them the most; who saved them and obtained eternal life for them? There is only one true central figure of world history, Jesus, the Son of God, the man of the cross! His incarnation is the turning point of our reckoning of time.

When the long axis of the Southern Cross is extended, it indicates the position of the celestial pole, the pivot of the earth's axis of rotation. In the same way the cross of Jesus is the pivotal point of our salvation. There is only one axis around which the starry skies rotate, and there is only one way of salvation, through the cross. Christ is the answer to all religious attempts to save oneself. He alone is the Way to the Father. All other paths are false, and lead to perdition. There is only one axis of salvation, and that is Christ (Acts 4:12). This fact is illustrated in the southern sky.

3. *The treasure in the field:* In one verse, Matthew 13:44, Jesus compares the treasure in a field with the kingdom of heaven. This invaluable treasure is not easily found on the highways of this world. In the enormous expanse of the starry skies God put a small treasure chest to remind us of these words of Jesus. This treasure is only found near the cross, and nowhere else in the vast expanse of the sky. This celestial Jewel Box is a parable of the kingdom of heaven.

4. *Heaven or hell:* The cross is the place of crucial decisions. The choice is between heaven and hell: "For the message of the cross is foolishness to those who are perishing, but to us who are being saved it is the power of God" (1 Cor 1:18). The decisions made by the two criminals hanging close to Jesus, made an eternal difference. In a very short time and in a very confined space one of them chose heaven when he cried out, "Jesus, remember me when You come into your kingdom" (Luke 23:42). But the other one persisted in his sin and thus chose the way to hell. Jesus describes hell as a place of darkness: "… throw him outside, into the darkness, where there will be weeping and gnashing of teeth" (Matt 22:13). The Coal Sack lies close to the Southern Cross; it is a sign of the place of darkness. God has written in the sky a warning against the place of perdition.

5. *Preaching the Gospel:* The two pointer stars point to the Southern Cross. One could thus ask who was the greatest "pointer" to the Saviour's cross? It certainly was Paul: "but we preach Christ crucified" (1 Cor 1:23). For him the message of salvation through the cross was the central theme of his ministry. He did not want to talk about anything else: "For I resolved to know nothing while I

was with you except Jesus Christ and him crucified" (1 Cor 2:2). Referring to the cross, he reprimanded the "foolish" Galatians: "Before your very eyes Jesus Christ was clearly portrayed as crucified" (Gal 3:1). Paul unceasingly emphasised the significance of the cross (Gal 5:1 & 6:14, Eph 2:16, Phil 2:8 & 3:18, Col 1:20 & 2:14). He is the most powerful witness for the cross – Like Alpha Centauri, Paul is the unrivalled "pointer" to the cross. The second pointer is the unnamed author of the Epistle to the Hebrews (e. g. Hebr 12:2); for all we know, it could have been Paul himself. Peter and John also describe the way of salvation in their epistles, but they do not use the word *cross* explicitly. In the sky, too, then there is more than one pointer to the cross.

6. *The cross on the earth:* The cross stood here on this earth, and not elsewhere in the universe. The cross of redemption was erected exactly here where man had fallen into sin. God came close to us here on earth. And Alpha Centauri is the nearest star, thus also illustrating this idea.

9. The Star of Bethlehem

There are numerous prophecies about Jesus's coming to this world, and in Numbers 24:17 He is depicted as a rising star: "A star will come out of Jacob; a sceptre will rise out of Israel. He will crush the foreheads of Moab, the skulls of all the sons of Sheth." Stars, including the sun, are used three times as signs involving God's Son to indicate three unique historic events: His birth (Matt 2:2), his crucifixion (Luke 23:44-45), and his second coming (Matt 24:29-30).

The wise men from the east came to look for the newly born king of the Jews: "We saw his star in the east and have come to worship him" (Matt 2:2). There has been a lot of speculation about what star or what astronomical phenomenon could have been the star of Bethlehem. Some possibilities are:

Comets: Bright comets with long tails have always aroused interest and have stirred up emotions. They were regarded as harbingers of extraordinary events. Many artists took up this idea and in typical folklorist nativity scenes the stable in Bethlehem was depicted showing a bright comet with a long tail in the sky. But there were no comets at that time which could have been the star of Bethlehem. The only known bright comets around the beginning of the Christian era appeared in 44 BC, 17 BC, and AD 66. Moreover, comets were always regarded as omens of evil – catastrophes like wars and plagues.

Novae: When an inter-galactic star explodes or flares up, it may shine brightly for a longer or shorter period in a position where no star had been visible beforehand. Such a stellar flare is called a "nova", meaning a new star (plural: novae). Novae have been known since ancient times, but only two were observed around the beginning of the Christian era, namely in 134 BC and AD 173 [H6, p 8].

Conjunction of planets: On 17 December 1603 *Johannes Kepler* was watching the sky through his telescope. As the official mathematician and astronomer in Prague, he was fascinated when he observed that Jupiter and Saturn were very close together in the constellation of Sagittarius. Such a close approach is known as a "conjunction"[27]. Though this is not a frequent event, it does occur periodically[28]. *Kepler* was fascinated by this phenomenon and started to calculate the times of previous conjunctions, and discovered that a triple conjunction of Jupiter and Saturn occurred in 7 BC. *Kepler* was the first person who saw a possible connection with the Star of Bethlehem [S2, p 14]. His original publication was forgotten, but in 1925 *Paul Schnabel*, a German Orientalist, succeeded in deciphering a New-Babylonian tablet which was nearly 2000 years old. It was the "Sippar stellar almanac", compiled by the then famous school of astrology at Sippar on the Euphrates. The notes concerning the year 7 BC are of special interest. The event of the year was the triple conjunction of Jupiter and Saturn. Jupiter was regarded by many

---

27 **Conjunction** (Latin: *coniunctio* = joining; the apparent juxta-position of two planets or stars as seen from earth): The orbits of Jupiter and Saturn lie outside that of the earth, and it sometimes happens that the earth comes between the sun and these two planets. Because the orbital speed of the earth is much faster, both planets may appear to move "backwards". In addition, they seem to perform looping motions.

28 **Conjunctions of Jupiter and Saturn:** Approximately every 20 years these two planets approach each other in a single conjunction. Triple conjunctions (i. e. three approaches in one year) occur once in 258 years, each time in a different constellation of the zodiac. A triple conjunction in the same constellation occurs once in about 794 years (non-periodical with 258). Due to the considerable reciprocal interference of the two giant planets Jupiter and Saturn, no real periodicity is maintained. In the 20th century a triple conjunction was visible, namely on 15 August and 11 October 1940, and on 20 February 1941 [K2, p 64-65] in the sign of the Ram.

nations as the star of happiness and royalty, and according to an ancient Jewish tradition, Saturn was the protector of Israel. The constellation of Pisces, the Fishes, referred to a land lying to the west. We now seem to be close to an explanation for the Star of Bethlehem:

On the 29th of May 7 BC the wise men observed the first close approach of Jupiter and Saturn from the roof of the school of astrology at Sippar. They combined Jupiter as the royal star, with Saturn, the protector of Israel, and concluded that a mighty king was born in the west (Pisces). So they decided to undertake the long and tedious journey to see for themselves that which they had discovered astronomically and had inferred astrologically. Many authors enthusiastically accept this explanation for the Star of Bethlehem (e.g. [F2, K1, K3, S2]). But is it so? My own conclusion is different: Nearly, but not quite, because such a view is not consistent with biblical doctrine.

In what follows, each of the three possibilities mentioned above will be discussed in the light of the biblical account. Let us now look very closely at the relevant passage:

> "The star they had seen in the east went ahead of them until it stopped over the place where the child was. When they saw the star, they were overjoyed. On coming to the house, they saw the child with his mother Mary, and they bowed down and worshipped him" (Matt 2:9-11).

This journey is now discussed with reference to four pertinent questions and we shall try to derive a biblically sound solution. It is necessary to consider all the given details seriously (as should be the case with all scriptural exegesis). Anything which is not specifically stated in the Bible, but which may be necessary to understand the circumstances, is tested against biblical doctrine.

1. Were the wise men astrologists? Presumably they belonged to the Babylonian profession of magi. As members of an important erudite priestly caste, they concerned themselves with pagan theology, with natural science in general, and with astronomy in particular. They were advisors of the king, and *Luther's* translation of the Greek *magos* into "wise man", is more suitable than the present-day perception that they were "magi" who were exclusively concerned with sorcery and occult practices. The wise men described in the New Testament, clearly were not wizards or soothsayers who practised the detestable art of astrology (Deut 18:11-12). They did not regard the stars as gods, but they realised that the stars were signs, and they wanted to worship or pay tribute to that person (the Greek word *proskyneo* means to prostrate oneself) to whom the stars directed them. Even today the sixth of January is celebrated as the day of the three kings. But the Bible does not mention three persons, nor that they were kings. These attributes were postulated by the fifth century Church and again in the eighth century, when they even received the names of Caspar, Melchior, and Balthasar.

2. What sources of information did the wise men have? The symbolic meaning of the star as indicative of the birth of the King of the Jews was for them such a certainty that they undertook a very tedious and long journey through desert areas. They must have been on the road for at least 60 days to cover the distance of about 800 km with their caravan. It was extremely important for them to find this new-born king. Many exegetes are of the opinion that the wise men accepted the contemporary view that Jupiter = the royal star, and Saturn = the star of Israel. When these two planets were in conjunction, they then concluded that the king of the Jews was born. But the Bible refers to a single star, and even at their closest approach on 1 June, 27 September, and 10 December in 7 BC, Jupiter and Saturn were still one full degree apart (see *Figure 7*), as has been determined by means of a computer. This angular separation is five times the distance between Alkor and Mizar, two stars which can be distinguished with the bare eye – see Chapter 3 para 12. Jupiter and Saturn were clearly discernible as two separate stars. They are separated by 1° which corresponds to two full moon diameters! *K.-F. Hoffmann* [H6, p 18], an astronomer, has pointed out that this conjunction is often deliberately made fuzzy in planetarium presentations to create the impression of a single "star".

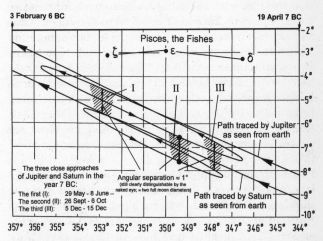

Figure 7: *The triple conjunction of Jupiter and Saturn. Even when closest, Saturn and Jupiter are separated by 1° which corresponds to two full moon diameters.*

Another argument against a conjunction of planets being the Star of Bethlehem, is the fact that such events occur regularly. But the birth of Jesus was a unique, never-to-be-repeated event. It is therefore highly improbable that God would have used a periodically repetitive astronomical phenomenon as a sign of the birth of His Son.

Furthermore, *Herod* summoned all the high priests and scribes (the Jewish Council) to find out "where the Christ was to be born" (Matt 2:3-4). *Herod* was an Edomite, appointed by the Romans; he was not a Jew. So why did he enquire about the birth of the Christ, and not the birth of a Jewish king? Herod could only have obtained the information that this new-born king and the Messiah was one person, from one of the wise men (or from his Jewish advisors). And where did these travellers from afar obtain this knowledge? Clearly, the conjunction of the two planets could not have pointed to the Messiah. Only God Himself could have revealed this to them. God did speak to them, as is clear from Matthew 2 verse 12. Only this can explain why these wise men travelled to such a small and insignificant country which was occupied by foreigners. It is significant that the term "King of the Jews" is only used on one other occasion in the New Testament, namely during the trial and crucifixion of Christ. Pilate asked Jesus whether He was the king of the Jews (Matt 27:11, Mark 15:2, Luke 23:3, John 18:33). And he asked the people whether he should release "the king of the Jews" (Mark 15:9, John 18:39). The Roman soldiers ridiculed Him with this title, and Pilate prepared a notice in three languages, Aramaic, Latin, and Greek, which declared that Jesus of Nazareth was the King of the Jews (John 19:19, Matt 27:37, Mark 15:26, Luke 23:38). Jesus is the eternal "Lord of lords and King of kings" (Rev 17:14, Rev 19:16). His earthly life between birth and death was characterised by the title "King of the Jews", as Jesus acknowledged before Pilate (John 18:37). It is noteworthy that this title was only used by pagans: The wise men from the east, Pilate the Roman Procurator, and the Roman soldiers.

3. What kind of object was the Star of Bethlehem? The star guided the wise men for several weeks until they came to Jerusalem. At that time the exact location was not yet revealed by God. This they only obtained after the conference of Herod with the priests and the scribes: Bethlehem! After this indication the star became a precise lodestar. The star which they had seen in the east and which urged them on in their westward journey, now guided them directly to a certain house (Greek *oikia* = house or cave). Whereas the star previously went ahead of them, it now came to a definite stop: "it stopped over the place where the child was" (Matt 2:9). At their destination the star itself behaved like a satellite. The only way that some celestial object can seem to stay in one position, is like a satellite in a synchronous orbit around the earth. All other known astronomical objects (the fixed stars, planets, and comets) seem to follow a certain course across the sky; they are thus unsuitable to indicate a specific position on earth or to act as an enduring direction indicator. This immediately excludes all known astronomical objects and configurations. The Star of Bethlehem could therefore only have been a luminous sign specifically created to guide the wise men, "for nothing is impossible with God" (Luke 1:37). If one tries to explain this episode in earthly terms only, without acknowledging God's supremacy, then many of the details supplied in the New Testament do not fit. In the Old Testament there is a similar example of the way God guided people in the direction He wanted them to go, namely during the exodus of the Israelites from Egypt. He guided them by means of a pillar of fire by night and a cloud by day; in this way He determined their speed and direction (Ex 13:21-22).

One other point still has to be clarified. In Matthew 2:6 Bethlehem is referred to as "by no means least among the rulers of Judah" (i. e. not a small town), whereas in Micah 5:2 it is described as "small among the clans of Judah". Is this an erroneous quotation, or was Matthew ill-informed? On the contrary, another historical example may explain this. In Belgium, south of Brussels, there is a place called Waterloo. At the beginning of the 19th century it was unknown and insignificant. But on June 18, 1815, when *Wellington* and *Blücher* defeated *Napoleon*, this changed completely. Since then Waterloo is mentioned in practically all history books and encyclopaedias, and many cities have erected Waterloo memorials to commemorate this victory over *Napoleon*. The first time Bethlehem is mentioned in the Old Testament, is as the burial place of Rachel (Gen 35:19). The next time it was referred to as the home of David's father (1 Sam 16:1). After the return from exile in Babylon there were only 123 men in Bethlehem (Ezra 2:21); it was a small town. In the time of Micah, 700 years before the birth of Jesus, Bethlehem was still a small village (Micah 5:1). But when the prophecy was fulfilled, Bethlehem acquired an important stature. Since the birth of God's Son Bethlehem is no longer insignificant (Matt 2:6). Most people – irrespective of nationality or religion – know about it.

4. Why did God guide these foreigners to Jerusalem where they caused such a stir? The account in Matthew 2:1-12 does not clarify this aspect, but we may derive two answers from the global testimony of the Bible:

(a) During the time of the Old Testament prophets God continually used different names for the promised Messiah to progressively reveal more of his nature (e.g. Seed of the woman, Saviour, Everlasting Father, Wonderful Counsellor, Prince of Peace, Lord of Israel, Sun of Righteousness). In John 5:39 Jesus refers to "the Scriptures that testify about me." And now the time was ripe (Gal 4:4); the Messiah was born. Surely God would have desired to divulge this information to his people. He then did something unusual: He told some foreign astronomers about the birth of his Son, and provided a special bright "star" as the sign. God instilled in them the desire to undertake a dangerous and tedious journey lasting many weeks to look for Jesus and honour Him as king. This brings them to Herod who is highly disturbed, so that he immediately convenes a meeting of all the high priests and scribes. Then, as a result of the quest on which the Orientals have embarked and were guided by God, they conclude that the Messiah has come. The "where" was known to them from Micah 5:1 (see Matt 2:4-6), and now the arrival of the men from the east was the sign that the previously unknown "when" had become "now".

They could then also have gone to Bethlehem to convince themselves of the correctness of their conclusion that the expected Christ had come to this world. They could have worshipped their Saviour and initiated a nation-wide campaign in the temple and in all synagogues to proclaim the wonderful news. Instead, they ignored this opportunity, and even withheld this important message of salvation from the people. Later Jesus exclaimed that they were lost: "You shut the kingdom of heaven in men's faces. You yourselves do not enter, nor will you let those enter who are trying to" (Matt 23:13).

(b) The wise men from the east did not belong to the chosen nation of Israel. They did not even know of a Saviour from guilt and sin. But when they heard about the Messiah, they immediately went to Jesus to worship Him. The Bible is quite clear about the following: "Everyone who calls on the name of the Lord (Jesus) will be saved" (Rom 10:13). These men found salvation, and their course of action is an example to us. In addition, God makes it clear that his plan of salvation is meant for all nations.

10. Who Created the Stars?

We have concluded that God created everything. The biblical creation account begins with the sentence: "In the beginning God created the heavens and the earth." This is quite correct, but it comprises only the introductory words of God's creation narrative. Later in the Bible the Person of the Creator is progressively revealed in more detail.

Creation and the Word of God: An attentive reading of the Bible reveals that statements about creation are often linked to explanations about the Word of God[29]. For example, the first part of Psalm 19 deals with creation, and the second part, from verse 7 onwards, immediately becomes a hymn of praise of the "statutes of the Lord" (i. e. God's Word). In Nehemiah 9 verse 3 the way the Israelites treated the "Book of the Law", is described; it is followed in verse 6 by a hymn extolling the Creator: "You alone are the Lord. You made the heavens, even the highest heavens, and all their starry host, the earth and all that is on it, the seas and all that is in them. You give life to everything, and the multitudes of heaven worship You." Further examples of such a close link are found in Psalm 33:4 & 6, Romans 1:16 & 20, Revelation 4:11 & 5:1. Then in Psalm 33:6 we find the reason for this connection: "By the Word of the Lord were the heavens made, their starry host by the breath of his mouth." The deepest and clearest revelation of these creative acts is found in the New Testament:

---

29 **The Word:** The world was made by the Word. God could easily have made light in silence, but He spoke and said: "'Let there be light', and there was light" (Gen 1:3). The words "And God said" or "Then God said" appear ten times in the creation account. In the New Testament more is said about this: "The Word was God" (John 1:1). In John 1:4 it is implied that life was in the Word.

"In the beginning was the Word, and the Word was with God, and the Word was God. He was with God in the beginning. Through Him all things were made; without Him nothing was made that has been made" (John 1:1-3).

Creation and Jesus: This "Word" is not a well-formulated sentence, neither is it a command or a speech, but it is a Person, a "He". Some verses further the clarifying statement follows: "He was in the world, and … the world was made through Him" (John 1: 10). This Logos is Jesus Christ! The first reference to Jesus as Creator in the Old Testament is found in the first chapter of the Bible, where the plural form is used: "Let US make man" (Gen 1:26). God the Father created through his Son, as is explained elsewhere: "For us there is but one God, the Father, from whom all things came and for whom we live; and there is but one Lord, Jesus Christ, through whom all things came and through whom we live" (1 Cor 8:6).

In Colossians 1:16-17 the creative acts of Jesus are taken further to include the origin of the for us still invisible world:

"For by him (Jesus Christ) all things were created: things in heaven and on earth, visible and invisible, whether thrones or powers or rulers or authorities; all things were created by him and for him. He is before all things, and in him all things hold together."

The beginning of the epistle to the Hebrews also testifies to the creative activity of Jesus:

"In these last days He has spoken to us by his Son, Whom He appointed heir of all things, and through Whom He made the universe" (Hebr 1:2).

The question of the origin of the stars has now been answered clearly: Jesus Christ is their Creator! Many people probably do not accept this idea, but it is taught unequivocally in the New Testament.

The stars did not originate in a "big bang" (see Appendix A2), nor during a subsequent random evolutionary process as has been proposed by people who do not acknowledge God. But the stars were purposefully planned and made by the Son of God.

A concept that surpasses our understanding: It is noteworthy that the astronomical symbol for the earth is a cross standing on a circle. This is a very aptly chosen sign, because the cross of Calvary was erected on a very special place in the universe: It did not stand somewhere in the empty reaches of a distant galaxy, neither was it erected on Jupiter or Saturn. No, it stood on this earth, the most important planet in God's view, the place where He created man. It was here that man fell into sin, and where redemption was and is required. No human being could achieve this. Only Someone Who came from heaven (the invisible dwelling place of God, not to be confused with the visible heaven containing the stars), was able to do this. Being without sin, the Son of God could do this, and He did do it out of his infinite love. God's love culminated on the cross. There God made "him who had no sin, to be sin for us" (2 Cor 5:21). *Martin Luther* expressed it as follows: "Your debts can only be in one of two places: Either on the Crucified Redeemer, or on yourself."

This unique redemptive act of God had been prophesied 750 years previously by Isaiah[30]:

> "He was despised and rejected by men,
> a man of sorrows, and familiar with suffering.
> Like one from whom men hide their faces
> he was despised, and we esteemed him not.
> Surely he took up our infirmities and carried our
> sorrows,

---

30 **Isaiah:** In Chapter 6 Isaiah describes his calling in the year of king Uzziah's death. This was approximately 740 BC, and he was active for more than 40 years, during the reign of kings Jotham, Ahaz, and Hezekiah.

yet we considered him stricken by God,
smitten by him, and afflicted.
But he was pierced for our transgressions,
he was crushed for our iniquities;
the punishment that brought us peace was upon
him,
and by his wounds we are healed.
We all, like sheep, have gone astray,
each of us has turned to his own way;
and the LORD has lain on him the iniquity of us all.
He was oppressed and afflicted,
yet he did not open his mouth;
he was led like a lamb to the slaughter,
and as a sheep before her shearers is silent,
so he did not open his mouth."

Isaiah 53:3-7

Our conclusion is breathtakingly amazing. The truth, which could not have been deduced by a mere human being, is that **the Man on the cross and the Creator of the entire universe is one and the same Person.** Who can really grasp this? When Jesus bore the sin of the world on the cross, the sun became dark for three hours. What an incredible situation! The Creator abased Himself to hang on the cursed tree. For our sakes He was crushed and became powerless. We feel like crying out with the psalmist: "How precious to me are your thoughts, O God! How vast is the sum of them! Were I to count them, they would outnumber the grains of sand" (Ps 139:17-18). Even though it may be difficult to understand that the Creator came to us as the Crucified Christ, we still have to consider the important question of the possibility of a personal relationship with Him. Is it true that the Creator is incredibly far away? The German poet *Schiller* placed Him above the stars in the firmament – "überm Sternenzelt". This question is discussed in the following chapter.

11. Knowing the Creator Personally

The previous chapters have left us with a lasting impression of a great God. Both the immensity of creation and the finer details of His works are far above our comprehension. Already in the Old Testament it is mentioned that God made everything through Christ (Wisdom, Proverbs 8:27-30). He is the actual "Works Supervisor" of creation. This concept is developed further in the New Testament. It surpasses our understanding that the Creator became a human being, and yet still is God Almighty.

Is it possible to find God? According to many poets and philosophers and the gloating authors of atheistic papers, God is an old man in whom nobody really believes any more (the German poet *Wolfgang Borchert:* Draußen vor der Tür), or that He died long ago *(Friedrich Nietzsche)*. But God Himself said and did everything necessary for those who really want to find Him. He has revealed Himself to many people: Moses, Abraham, Isaac, Jacob, David, ... We read in Hebrews 1:1-2: "In the past God spoke to our forefathers through the prophets at many times and in various ways, but in these last days He has spoken to us by his Son." In Hebrews 12:1 "a great cloud of witnesses" is mentioned; this cloud refers to all the many people who had met God and believed in Him long before our time. God's purpose is very clear: "God our Saviour, ... wants all men to be saved and to come to a knowledge of the truth" (1 Tim 2:3-4). His greatest outreach towards lost mankind was initiated with the coming of Jesus. Christ describes his incarnation in the following words: "For the Son of Man came to seek and to save what was lost" (Luke 19:10). The adversary is also seeking, but his purpose is quite the opposite; he wants to destroy: "The devil prowls around like a roaring lion looking for someone to devour" (1 Peter 5:8).

The Bible is full of promises for those who are seeking God. Somebody has expressed it as follows: If you take one step towards God, He then takes a thousand steps towards you. God has emphasised that the seeker shall find Him, as is clear from several texts:

Deuteronomy 4:29: "But if ... you seek the LORD your God, you will find Him if you look for Him with all your heart and with all your soul."

Proverbs 8:17: "I love those who love Me, and those who seek Me, find Me."

Amos 5:4: "Seek Me and live."

Matthew 7:7-8: "Ask and it will be given to you; seek and you will find; knock and the door will be opened to you. For everyone who asks, receives; he who seeks, finds; and to him who knocks, the door will be opened."

John 6:37: "Whoever comes to me, I will never drive away."

Using three examples of seekers, we will now explain how God may be found. The first example is the episode of the Ethiopian official as described in Acts 8:26-39. The following rendition is based on this conversation[31], and it could well have happened as described below:

---

31 **Biblical dialogues:** Many conversations are described in the Bible, especially between Jesus or the apostles and other persons. Jesus always had time for those people who came to Him. He never ended a conversation because of a lack of time. In the New Testament only the essentials, or the result, of such conversations are reported. For example, the exhaustive dialogue in the night between Jesus and Nicodemus is described in only 21 verses (John 3:1-21), and

1. The Ethiopian treasurer: He had heard about God, but he did not know Him. When he heard that God could be found in Jerusalem, he decided to go there. There were no international flights at that time, so he decided to undertake this costly and tedious journey through deserts and inhospitable regions. He carefully got a caravan together with all necessities. No expense or effort was too great, because his search for God was to him a serious matter. If this Creator-God really existed, he wanted to know Him. After several weeks his journey ended in Jerusalem. Where could he look for God? On the market-places, on the Mount of Olives, in the temple? He met and observed many people, from labourers and merchants to priests; he spoke to the devout as well as to unbelievers. But he did not find God anywhere. Eventually, disappointed and exasperated, he resumed his homeward journey without having achieved his goal. It seems probable that he decided to get a souvenir of this big city to take home with him. He then bought a scroll without bothering to scrutinise it. His main consideration was that at least he now had something special to remind him of his visit to Jerusalem, a foreign city far from home.

On his homeward journey he remembered this scroll, and he wondered what it was about. He settled down com-

---

the conversation describing the conversion of Matthew, is condensed into one verse (Matt 9:9). We can be sure that Jesus fully answered all questions of any seeker. His apostles did likewise. If everything that Jesus did and said were written down, all the books in the world would probably not be enough (John 21:25). Exactly because the biblical accounts and conversations are brief, there is plenty of freedom for sermons. This freedom may be utilised for the purpose of explaining the Gospel message in present-day terms. However, everything must be structured in such a way that the overall message of the Bible is not contradicted. The following expansion of the dialogue between Philip and the Ethiopian should be understood in this way. It is also necessary to point out that the actual quotations from the New Testament were not yet available in written form when this conversation took place, but they are included for a better understanding.

fortably in his chariot to study it. He read aloud, because here in the empty desert there was no need to worry about other people. He had learnt Hebrew some years ago so that individual words were no problem. He opened the scroll randomly, and started reading from Isaiah 53, which he found to be quite remarkable. A certain "HE" is mentioned repeatedly. HE took up our infirmities; HE bore our sorrows; HE … HE … HE … Who could HE be? His name was not mentioned at all.

Suddenly somebody approaches. Where could he have come from in this desolate place? How was it possible for a traveller to wander alone in this burning desert? The stranger came directly to the Ethiopian and he was visibly touched by the words which he had overheard. He briefly introduces himself: "My name is Philip."

The following lively and protracted dialogue between Philip (P) and the Ethiopian (E) now ensues:

P: Do you know what you are reading?

E: I have read many books in my life, but I can't make head nor tail of this text. Obviously something very important is described, but I do not understand it. Could you possibly explain it to me?

P: Yes, I can. You might not believe it, but I personally know this man you are reading about. I have even seen Him a few times and I have never before met someone who spoke with such authority, and with so much love. His deeds also touched me deeply.

E: But that is impossible. Are you trying to make fun of me? According to the book merchant in Jerusalem this scroll is more than 700 years old. On reading this section, I wondered whether the author wrote about himself or about someone he knew, and I found it rather confusing. But now that you say you know this person, I am thoroughly mixed up. How am I to understand this?

P: I appreciate your position. It is difficult to tie all the ends together, but I am surely telling the truth. Many people have studied this text (Isaiah 53), and over the years many scrolls have been filled with commentaries. You may be amazed, but I can give you the real answer about this "HE" and his circumstances. The prophet Isaiah wrote about the expected Messiah, the Saviour Who would come just as God had been promising for centuries. Just imagine, He came right now during our lifetime. He was born in Bethlehem, not far from Jerusalem. (This was also announced about 750 years ago by God through the prophet Micah (Micah 5:1), a contemporary of Isaiah.) When the Messiah was thirty years old, He called twelve men to follow Him. When his followers were still learning, He named them his disciples. He proclaimed God's good news all over the country. Although He did not go to a high school nor study at a university, I have never before heard anyone who could preach and teach like He did. But He did not just talk, He also healed many seriously ill people. I myself observed only a few such healings, but my namesake was one of the twelve, and he has told me everything in detail, so that I now feel that I have been present all along. For example, he described an astonishing experience they had on the Sea of Galilee: "Once a severe storm battered our boat, and we were terrified, expecting it to sink any moment. But He slept undisturbed, as if the storm did not bother Him at all. When we roused Him, He scolded us for our lack of faith. Then He raised his hand and rebuked the storm. The storm abated immediately and it became quiet and calm. We had never before experienced anything like this."

E: Please tell me more about Him; I really am interested.

P: On another occasion while they were travelling, they received the news that a good friend was severely ill in

Bethany. Remember, He had the power to heal all ailments immediately, as the disciples had often witnessed.

E: So they immediately went to Bethany?

P: Not at all! The disciples did not understand why He decided to stay where they were for a couple of days. They were afraid that his friend Lazarus, with whom they had become acquainted through Him, might die in the meantime. When they eventually did go to Bethany, that was exactly what had happened. Many friends, neighbours and relatives were already plunged in mourning. They cried and wailed as if the world had fallen apart. They were too late, and Lazarus's sister Martha exclaimed: "Lord, if You had been here, my brother would not have died." The disciples could hardly believe their eyes when they saw what happened next. Two commands were given; the first was: "Take away the stone." But Martha objected: "By this time there is a bad odour, for he has been there four days." But the Lord did not budge and the stone was rolled away. Then came the second command; He called in a loud voice: "Lazarus, come out!" All those who were present gasped in astonishment, for they had never seen anything like this. The dead man came forth immediately, still wrapped up as for burial.

E: Now tell me, why are you not with this man now? I would never leave such a man, but I would follow his every step.

P: I was expecting this question. He loved everybody like no one before Him. He did good deeds like nobody else anywhere. He never did anything evil. Not even his enemies could point out a single transgression. In spite of all this He was sentenced to death and was nailed to a cross while fully conscious.

E: But being so powerful, He could have defended Himself.

P: Yes, He could have, but He silently bore everything done to Him. He had informed his twelve disciples of his death long before, but they found it hard to believe that He had to suffer such a cruel death. He frequently explained that it had to happen like that; He had to die for man's sin. If He did not bear everybody's sins by dying on the cross, then all people would be lost and eternally doomed. He explained repeatedly that there was no other way of redemption from sin. He died some time ago, when He was crucified outside the gates of the city which you have visited. A Roman centurion was in charge of this terrible event. This fearless warrior had often conducted public executions, and he knew exactly how people reacted in such extreme circumstances. Screams and curses followed one another, punctuated with groans and gasps. He had often observed this drawn-out bitter battle with death. But what he saw now was very different from all his previous experiences. Now a very different person was dying. He did not in the least reproach his torturers. While the raging crowd derided Him, He prayed to his Father in heaven: "Forgive them, for they do not know what they are doing."

E: Pardon my interruption, but the sentence which I have read: "He did not open his mouth; He was led like a lamb to the slaughter", seems to fit this situation.

P: Yes, exactly! The prophet accurately described what I have been telling you. With his last breath He said: "It is finished", meaning that God's plan for the redemption of mankind has been carried out. Never before had anybody nailed to a cross said such words. Something quite unusual was happening, moving the centurion to exclaim: "Surely this man was the Son of

God!" Nobody told him this; it was his own conclusion.

E: If I may interrupt you again, I also believe this after hearing your account. He could not have been an ordinary man. It is obvious that my scroll refers to this Person who was crucified. But please continue, this is fascinating.

P: The best part has not yet been told: He did not stay in the grave. Because He never did anything wrong and really was without sin, death could not hold Him. He arose on the third day.

E: What did you say? Is He alive? But that is impossible! Were there any eyewitnesses?

P: Yes! His disciples were told beforehand, but they did not really understand it. There never was any reason to doubt his words, because everything He said, happened just like He predicted. He once said: "I am the … truth" (John 14:6). So when they saw the risen Lord, spoke to Him, touched Him, and even ate with Him, they were absolutely sure. Everything which He had told them, now made sense. In Bethany He had said: "I am the resurrection and the life", but at that time they could not understand this.

E: But where is He now? If He lives, I want to meet Him as soon as possible.

P: That is the most important and most burning question that anybody could ever ask. After he had risen from the grave, He commanded his disciples to tell the whole world about Him. His exact words were:

"All authority in heaven and on earth has been given to me. Therefore go and make disciples of all nations, baptising them in the name of the Father and of the Son and of the Holy Spirit, and teaching them to obey everything I have commanded you. And surely I will be with you always, to the very end of the age" (Matt 28:18-20).

After this commission He parted from the disciples and was taken away in a cloud, before their eyes, returning to his Father in heaven. While the disciples were still watching his ascent, two men in white clothes suddenly appeared. They were angels who comforted them: "Men of Galilee, why do you stand here looking into the sky? This … (man), who has been taken from you into heaven, will come back in the same way you have seen Him go into heaven" (Acts 1:11). He often told us that He will return at the end of time, and everyone will see Him. Then He will not come as a child, but in all his power and glory, to judge all people. Nobody will escape from this judgement.

E: You have told me many new things which will keep my mind occupied for a long time. But, tell me, if I have understood these things correctly, then it is important for everybody to turn to him. Can I do that? Did He also pay for my transgressions?

P: Your conclusion is correct. People from all nations and tongues and tribes will be saved when they come to Him, including the Ethiopians.

E: Something strikes me. We have spoken a lot about Him, and you only said "He" like in the scroll. Does He have a name at all?

P: O yes, He has a very special name, **Jesus**.

E: I have not heard this name before. It does not resemble any of the fine-sounding Ethiopian names I know.

P: There is something very special about this name. Even the prophets who wrote about Him under God's guidance, did not know his name. God kept this secret for a long time. It was only shortly before his birth that an angel told Mary that she would give birth to a son and that he should be called Jesus (Matt 1:21). God Himself elevated this name above all others (Jesus is the Greek form of Yashua, which means: "The Lord saves"). It is more than just an appealing name; it implies a wide variety of deeds and attributes. He often taught us Who He was: I am the Good Shepherd, I am the Light of the World, I am the Way to the Father, I am the Truth, I am the Life ... the name Jesus comprises all these concepts. Nobody on earth could ever before make such claims about himself. But these words aptly describe his life and being. He really was the Saviour, the Christ promised by God. "Therefore God exalted Him to the highest place and gave Him the name that is above every name" (Phil 2:9). And whoever calls on this Name, will be saved.

E: I have to mention the purpose of my journey once more. At home I had already heard that there is a God. I looked for Him in Jerusalem for several days. I wanted to worship Him, but I did not find Him anywhere. Can you tell me the way to God?

P: I have already told you that Jesus is the Way, the only way! There is no other way that leads to God. Our own attempts to find Him otherwise, are fruitless. God stepped down to meet us through Jesus, and faith in Him will bring us to God (Rom 3:22-26). "Salvation is found in no one else, for there is no other name under heaven given to men by which we must be saved" (Acts 4:12).

E: Do I understand you correctly that it is impossible to go to God directly? Is Jesus the only way?

P: Yes, exactly! If you seek God apart from Jesus, then you ignore God's will. He has sent his Son Jesus so that we may receive eternal life from Him. Jesus was empowered to do this when He died on the cross; He alone is able to give this gift of everlasting life.

E: It has now become clear to me why the pious Pharisees and Sadducees could not show me the way to God. They talked about Him a lot, but they did not know Him, because they rejected Him.

P: Now you have come very close to salvation. Pray to the Lord Jesus, confess your sins, and invite Him into your life.

E: After everything I have now heard, I really would like to do that. (He now prays and tells Jesus everything in an impassioned prayer.)

P: Now you have become a child of God. Jesus is your Saviour, and God is your heavenly Father. When you are a child of God, you will inherit heaven. Your wealth is now greater than that of the Queen of Ethiopia!

E: I still cannot really understand what has happened to me. I feel like jumping from the wagon for joy. Can you believe it? What a coincidence! I bought this Isaiah scroll without knowing what a treasure it was. And exactly when I was reading about the Son of God, the Redeemer, and could not understand it, then you turned up to guide me. Furthermore, God's plan of salvation has only recently been fulfilled. All this is impossible to believe, were it not for God.

P: You have sought God wholeheartedly, and He has promised that anybody who did that, would find Him. You have experienced this, and I have to tell you another important thing about Jesus, Who has now become your Lord. When you look up into the sky tonight and see the glittering stars, remember that they were created by Someone you now know personally: the Creator of this wonderful universe is none other than the same Jesus who bore our sins on the cross. Everything comes together in his Person: He is the Saviour and the Redeemer, He is the Crucified and the Risen Christ, and He is also the Creator of this earth and of the entire universe with all its stars.

E: Will this amazement never stop? You have told me more and more wonderful things about my new Lord.

But I have one more question. At one stage you said something about being baptised. Please tell me more about that; what exactly is it?

P: I will do that gladly, because Jesus Himself has explained it. When one has come to faith in Christ, the next logical step is to be baptised. By this act you publicly proclaim, before visible and invisible witnesses, that you have voluntarily come to Jesus. Then you belong to Him for life and for ever. Baptism means that you have entered a new sphere of life, laying down the old life which was without Christ (Rom 6:4). Faith and baptism are inseparable, as Jesus said: "Whoever believes and is baptised, will be saved" (Mark 16:16). Baptism thus is an act of obedience.

E: Look, there is water over there. I want to go all the way. If you regard me as a believer, then please baptise me.

P: You have definitely accepted Jesus; you are now a believer, and I will gladly baptise you on the strength of your avowal. Stop the chariot, then we can both go into the water, where I will baptise you in the name of God, your Father in heaven, his Son Jesus, your Saviour, and the Holy Spirit, Who will henceforth guide you in all truth. You should note the following symbolic meanings: Immersion in the water signifies our being dead with Christ, for "All of us who were baptised into Christ Jesus were baptised into his death" (Rom 6:3). And when you emerge from the water, it may be seen as a representation of your resurrection: "If the spirit of Him who raised Jesus from the dead is living in you, (then) He who raised Christ from the dead will also give life to your mortal bodies through his Spirit, who lives in you" (Rom 8:11).

E: I am truly grateful that I did find God at last, after having resignedly embarked on my homeward journey.

Now here in this barren desert I have found God in Jesus. I can hardly believe it, but it has become clear to me that God is not bound to a certain place. We can find Him anywhere if we really want to, but He can only be found in Jesus, and nowhere else. My heart is overflowing with joy! This has been the most important journey of my life, and I am taking this good news home to my countrymen.

The most important conclusions to be drawn from this account, are:

– When you really seek God, you will find Him.

– When you really seek God, you will find Him in Jesus.

– When you seek Jesus, you will find Him in the Word of God, the Bible.

– Only those who have found Jesus are redeemed.

– When you accept Jesus, you become a child of God.

– When you believe in Jesus, you have eternal life.

Next I want to relate two personal experiences which the reader might find informative and useful:

2. Scaling a wall: During an evangelical outreach in the town hall of Braunschweig I invited the audience to make a personal decision for Christ. Several persons came to the counselling area. A tall and lean octogenarian, called *Bernhard*, told me that he understood everything I had said, but that he could not come to Jesus, because there was a great wall of objections which obstructed the way. Then I simply asked him whether he wanted to scale the wall. He immediately answered: "Yes!" My response was: "If you really want to, then I can guarantee that you will find God today, not because I say so, but on the strength of God's promises." I then explained the way to God by means of basic biblical affirmations like that found in John 14:6: The only way is through Jesus. After all his questions had been answered, we prayed to Jesus, and I noticed that his eyes were shining. Something was happening; he exclaimed joyfully that he had scaled the wall. He could hardly believe it that the obstacles had disappeared. He found salvation because he sincerely desired it. He has been a member of our congregation for a long time now, and whenever we meet each other, we are reminded of that wall which had seemed to be an insurmountable obstacle. In the words of Psalm 18:29: "With my God I can scale a wall."

3. At what moment have I been saved? After a sermon I gave at Bad Gandersheim (Germany), one of the guests came to me, a lady with the name of *Dorothea*. She had dutifully attended the Sunday devotions, but was disturbed by some of my words. Our conversation went more or less as follows:

She: I regard myself as a believer and have believed in God for a long time already, but you repeatedly emphasised the necessity of a personal relationship with Jesus. I find that rather difficult to do and I have never prayed to Jesus. Is that really necessary when one in any case prays to God? I have even experienced answered prayers.

I: It is right that you believe in God and pray to Him. He has promised that He would help those who call on Him when they are distressed (Ps 50:15). He reveals Himself as the good God, and thus we may trust Him, as you have experienced.

She: Then I have done the right things. But why do you emphasise Jesus so strongly?

I: God Himself has presented Jesus in a unique way. On the mountain of the transfiguration God declared: "This is my Son, whom I love; with Him I am well pleased. Listen to Him!" (Matt 17:5). Later God said that we should believe in the Lord Jesus, as we read in Romans 3:25: "God presented Him as a sacrifice of atonement, through faith in his blood." If we do not come to Jesus, then we continue to live in our sinful state. Jesus Himself said in John 16:9 that the real sin of mankind is that "men do not believe in Me." The obvious conclusion is that it is God's will that we must believe in the Lord Jesus Christ. This means that we should have communion with Him, pray to Him, and live with Him. Without Him we cannot enter heaven, because He alone is the Way to the Father, as He has emphasised (John 14:6). We can only be saved through Jesus, and we can only obtain redemption when we believe in Him. Even before we are converted, God reveals his grace to us because He loves us. He wants to make it clear that He is interested in us and wants to draw us to Him. In the words of Romans 2:4: "God's kindness leads you towards repentance." There is thus no contradiction when God answers our prayers even before we have been saved.

She: So if I don't believe in Jesus, then I am disobedient to God?

I: Yes, exactly. Without Jesus you cannot be a child of God; you cannot be saved. It is unambiguously stated in John 3:36: "Whoever believes in the Son (of God) has eternal life, but whoever rejects the Son (of God) will not see life, for God's wrath remains on him." In just two verses, Acts 16:14-15, Lydia's conversion is described. Her situation was similar to yours: She believed in God and kept his commandments. But was she saved? It was only after Paul had explained the Gospel message, that she accepted Christ as her Lord and was then saved.

She: Now I understand what was lacking in my life, and I wish to accept the Lord Jesus right now. Please help me. (She then prayed to Jesus to confirm her decision.)

Seeking God: Many people are seeking God. Many find Him, as explained in the previous examples, but others are not so fortunate. The various experiences are illustrated in *Figure 8*. In Chapter 8.1 (Does the Universe Require a Creator?) we referred to poets, physicists, and astronomers who thought about God, but did not find Him, the Father of Jesus Christ, because they looked in the wrong places. It is all right to seek in various places, but eventually one should come to the only place where the promise can be fulfilled (Jeremiah 29: 13-14).

Someone was looking for a lost key in the light cast by a street lamp, but he could not find it. When he was asked if this was where he had lost the key, he said: "No, but at least I have enough light here."

This describes the situation of many God-seekers. If you seek God in the multitude of worldly religions, you will find the "god of the religions": Names like Zeus, Aphrodite, Allah, Krishna, Shiwa, Manitu, or Buddha, but you will not find the God of the Bible. *Hoimar von Ditfurth* wrote much about the god he sought in evolution and who was for him the author of evolution. It is clear from his own affirmations that he did not know the God of the Bible, therefore he found and devised the "god of evolution" (discussed more fully in [G8, p 89-109]). Poets and philosophers have developed their own and differing ideas about God, but they still did not find the God of the Bible. All God-seekers who pursue their own ideas, end up with idols which cannot provide salvation. There is yet another way of not finding God: If you deliberately reinterpret the message of the Bible, criticise it, or reject it. Philosophers such as *Sartre, Camus, Feuerbach, Marx*, and *Bloch* did just that. The Marxist philosopher *Ernst Bloch* devised the headline: "A new god has come into being".

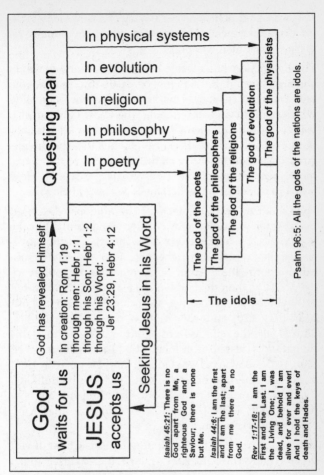

Figure 8: *Man seeking God.*

133

This was his conclusion after having changed many biblical pronouncements and omitted others. Eventually he declared that man was god.

The living God has revealed Himself in many ways: in creation, through his servants on earth, through his Son, and through his Word. There are many signs in creation which point to God, and people who know Him can also lead us to God. But we will only find Him in Jesus, as has been explained above. It is also obvious that the Bible is crucially important. After all that has now been said, one more question should be resolved by the reader: How may I personally be saved? This is discussed below.

How do I find Jesus in practice? The situations described in the three examples above, differ significantly, but the outcome is the same in every case. The act of turning to Jesus is called repentance in the Bible. It means that we submit our entire life to Him; He becomes Lord of our every deed, desire, thought, and word. He never forces Himself on anybody, but He is always knocking at the door of our heart (Rev 3:20), and waits until we pray to Him, inviting Him to take the reins as Lord of our life. The result of this invitation is described in John 1:12: "To all who received Him, to those who believed in his name, He gave the right to become children of God." You may now be thinking: I've known for a long time that I should repent, but how do I actually do it? This is now explained, so that every reader can become sure of his or her own salvation.

Call on the name of the Lord: pray to Jesus Christ. If you do not know how to pray, follow the example given below:

> *"Lord Jesus, I now understand who You are, the Creator of this world and of all life. Through You God created the entire universe and all the stars and constellations. Although You are the Creator of everything, You also are the Man who died on Calvary's cross for my sins.*

But death could not hold You. You arose from the grave and You are the almighty Lord, reigning everywhere. I beseech You now to become my personal Lord.

I know that I cannot stand before You and the Living God with my burden of sin, but You came to this world to save lost sinners. You paid the price on the cross so that I may be free and will not be doomed. I trust You in everything; my life is an open book before You. You know all my transgressions, all the false stirrings of my heart, as well as my indifference towards You. Now I pray with all my heart: Please forgive all my known and unknown sins, and please remove everything in my life which is wrong in your eyes. I thank You for your wonderful mercy and grace, that I may know right now that You have answered my prayer. You are Truth personified, and I believe the promises given in your Word.

Dear Lord Jesus, come now and fill my life. Guide me in the way that You will show me when I read the Bible. I know that You are the Good Shepherd and are concerned about my welfare, I therefore entrust my entire life to You: My thoughts and deeds, my occupation, my spare time, my plans, my friends, my finances, my health, my illnesses, my cares, my joys and my sorrows. Help me to break with my sinful way of life. And if I still have short-comings, help me to identify and confess them immediately. Please control my life and make me conscious of those things that please You and which You will bless in my life. Change my attitude towards You and towards all persons who cross my path daily. Give me an obedient heart, and open the Bible for me so that I will understand it correctly. Henceforth I acknowledge You as my Lord and I will follow You for ever. Amen."

If this prayer, or a similar one formulated by you, has been deeply sincere, then you have now become a child of God. "To all who received Him (the Lord Jesus), to those who believed in his Name, He gave the right to become children of God" (John 1:12). The real full life promised by God begins immediately. In addition, you now have eternal life. Even the heavenly hosts are involved in your conversion to Jesus Christ, as He says in Luke 15:10: "In the same way, I tell you, there is rejoicing in the presence of the angels of God over one sinner who repents."

The following advice is given to all (new) Christians:

1. Bible study: It is necessary to read the Bible daily to find out about God's will. It is the only book authorised by Him, and it provides nurture for continual spiritual growth. It would be best to begin with one of the New Testament Gospels; John's Gospel is recommended.

2. Prayer: You should pray to God and to Jesus Christ daily. It is a wonderful source of inner strength, and you will be changed. Everything should be taken to Jesus in prayer – all your cares, sorrows, joys and plans. Thank God for everything in your life. Bible study and prayer comprise the "circulatory system" which is of crucial importance for a healthy life of faith.

3. Fellowship: Seek the company of other known Christians regularly. A glowing ember is quickly extinguished when it is removed from the fire. Our love for Christ will also cool off when it is not continually replenished through fellowship with other believers. It is therefore necessary to be actively involved in a church community where the authority of the entire Bible is accepted wholeheartedly. Such fellowship is essential for our spiritual growth and for a healthy life of faith.

4. Obedience: The Bible is an inexhaustible source of helpful advice for all walks of life and for communion with God. If you follow this advice, you will be blessed richly. There is no better way of showing that we love God, than to obey Him: "This is love for God: to obey his commands" (1 John 5:3).

5. Witnessing: Tell others what Jesus means to you. Very many people have not yet accepted the Gospel of salvation; they need to see our example and hear our witnessing. In this way you are a fellow-worker of God.

It is great cause for joy if you have deliberately turned to Jesus Christ and have been accepted by God.

Repentance and conversion means that your life is henceforth characterised by a clean break with sin. *Paul Humburg* illustrated this change in railway terms: "Before our conversion we sin on schedule, but afterwards every sin is regarded as a disastrous derailment." However, not even a true Christian can live without sinning, as many people seem to expect. But the position of sin has changed drastically; now we fight against it (see for example 1 John 3:7-10 and Hebr 12:4). This new life leads to new attitudes and new priorities – the kingdom of God now occupies the central position. The Christian hungers after the words of God, and he seeks fellowship with other believers. He is guided by the Holy Spirit (Rom 8:14) and the fruit of the Spirit (Gal 5:22) becomes evident in his life. Conversion marks the end of the old life like the full-stop at the end of a sentence, and at the same time it introduces the new life like a colon. The New Testament describes it as follows: "If anyone is in Christ, he is a new creation" (2 Cor 5:17). Our earthly life becomes really meaningful. At the same time we receive the gift of being children of God; we inherit eternal life and will live with Jesus in heaven for ever and ever.

12. Conclusion

Our point of departure was, "Why have the stars been created?" and in the previous chapter we arrived at the question: "How may I enter heaven?" We have come full circle, encompassing both meanings of the Hebrew word *shamayim*. We have crossed over from the starry heavens to God's heaven, and the contents of this book can be expressed in a single sentence:

God has made the stars
so that we may enter into heaven.

Appendix

In the principal part of the book we were mainly concerned with the stars, as the title indicates. The earth which is our home, the planets and other bodies in our solar system, and the other planets were only briefly mentioned. In this appendix our "neighbours" in space are discussed more fully, because they are also extremely fascinating.

N. Pailer, a German astronomer, writes [P2, p 1]: "In recent years space probes have gathered more information about the solar system than was possible during the previous 2,000 years in the history of astronomy. They orbited around planets and dropped recording equipment. Within a brief period a new view of the solar system emerged from the streams of data, and the numerous close-up photographs of the planets and their rings and moons." Our solar system with its 9 planets (or even 11 planets; see chapter A1.3, point 18) and 66 moons (figures known when going to press in 1993) comprises abundant evidence of its uniqueness, some of which will now be discussed. For obvious reasons we start with the earth itself and its relationships to the sun and the moon.

A1. Details of the Solar System

A1.1 The Earth – an Exceptional Planet

Three centuries ago *Gottfried Wilhelm Leibniz* (1646 – 1716), who was an all-round scientist, said that our earth was the best of all possible worlds. At that time he could not fully realise the aptness and correctness of this statement. Only recently, as a result of new scientific findings, it became clear that the physical and chemical conditions prevailing on earth, as well as its astronomical relationships, are eminently suitable for life on our home planet. Some selected aspects should emphasise the uniqueness of the earth:

1. The correct distance from the sun: The average distance of the earth from the sun is approximately 150 million km. The amount of light and heat radiated by the sun determines the prevailing temperatures on earth. If the sun were hotter, then this distance would have been too small and the earth would have been too hot for living organisms. If the sun were cooler, then the earth would have had to have been nearer to the sun to receive sufficient energy. The actual combination of distance and energy emission causes temperatures on earth to vary mostly between 0 °C and 40 °C. These are the narrow limits required to sustain life as we know it. There are organisms which can tolerate lower or higher temperatures, but they are the exceptions which prove the rule.

The earth's orbit around the sun is very nearly a perfect circle (the eccentricity, *e*, of the ellipse is only 0.0167). According to *Kepler's* laws, the orbit of a planet or comet may be an elongated ellipse with the sun at one focus (see *Figure 15*). In such a case the temperature would be very high at the point of closest approach, and very low at the outer end of the orbit. In the course of a year temperatures may for example reach 300 °C during a short, hot period (at the time of perihelion), and there would be a long, cold period (around aphelion). Life could not exist on a planet moving in an elongated elliptical orbit.

2. The correct speed of rotation of the earth: The correct distance from the sun is an insufficient condition for supporting life on earth. If the earth's rotation around its axis were slower, then the differences between the climate during night and day would be extreme. Temperatures would climb to intolerable heights during the day because of the prolonged influx of heat, and the surface would be desiccated. On the other hand, it would become very cold at night. If the earth's period of rotation were 48 hours for example, then all over the earth, in summer as well as in winter, frost would occur nightly, and noon temperatures would be very high. Such extremes of temperature can only be tolerated by very-short-lived organisms, if at all. Because of the actual relatively fast speed of rotation resulting in a 12-hour alternation between night and day, the temperatures thus even out at any given place. If the earth rotated at an appreciably higher speed, then the small differences between night and day would have a negative effect on weather cycles. In addition, the increased centrifugal forces would cause atmospheric gases to escape into space.

3. The correct length of the year: The length of the year suits our life cycles. The seasons are the correct length to ensure that there is enough time for growth between sowing and reaping, and the winter is not too long for man and animal to be able to subsist on stored supplies. The corresponding cycles on other planets make survival impossible. It is hard to imagine a year which is 84 years long as on Uranus, or lasting only 88 days as on Mercury.

4. The correct inclination of the earth's axis: The angle which the earth's axis makes with the plane of its orbit around the sun, is of crucial importance for life-sustaining conditions. Scientific calculations show that the optimum inclination of the earth's axis lies in the narrow interval between 23° and 24°. Is it a coincidence that the actual angle is exactly 23.5°? If this angle had been larger, the contrast between summer and winter would have been very much greater.

If the *axis of the earth were perpendicular to the plane of its orbit*, then there would have been no seasonal variations, but the influx of energy would vary markedly according to latitude. It would have been so hot at the equator that large areas around the tropics would be uninhabitable, and the cold desolate areas around the poles would have been much larger.

If the *earth's axis coincided with the plane of its orbit*, then daytime would have lasted six months on one side of the earth while it would be night on the other side. In such a situation the day would become intolerably hot, and no life could exist on the extremely cold night side. Only near the equator would there be any kind of day-and-night cycle, but under extreme conditions. Winter would occur twice per year, when the sun would be close to the horizon as seen from the equator. Uranus and Pluto are examples of such an extreme inclination of the axis of rotation.

The actual inclination of 23.5° produces a stabilising succession of seasons so that the very hot and the inhospitably cold regions are relatively small.

It should be obvious that the celestial parameters of the earth are as beneficial as could be. This is already amazing, but there are many more crucial conditions in the set of requirements necessary for life on earth.

5. The correct mass and size of the earth: These two quantities are closely related, and their respective values make it possible for the earth to retain its atmosphere. The force of gravity on the surface is just right to ensure this, while it is too low on the moon. The acceleration due to gravity on the surface of the moon is only 1.63 m/s^2. The specific gravity of the earth is 5.517 g/cm^3 making it the densest of all the planets. If its diameter were 20 % less, then its mass would have been only half its present value. Then the gravitational acceleration on the surface would be only 7.85 m/s^2 instead of the present 9.81 m/s^2 and then most of the gases of the atmosphere would escape into space. Only the heavier gases like carbon dioxide and argon would remain. On the other hand, if the diameter of the earth were 25 % greater, then the mass of the earth

144

would be doubled, air pressure would be much higher, and our body weight would increase by 25 %.

With the same density, a doubling of the earth's diameter would result in an eight fold increase in its mass and the force of gravity on the surface. Atmospheric pressure and the pressure of the water vapour would also be eight times as high if the air mass per unit of surface area remained the same. The air would be much drier, because condensation in the form of clouds and rain would occur at much lower values of humidity. All living organisms would require much more energy for movement, and all skeletal loads (on knees and feet for example) would be much greater because of the increased weight.

6. The unique composition of the atmosphere: Oxygen makes up 21 % of the atmosphere, which is much greater than for any other planet. Oxygen is essential for the existence of higher life forms, but if the percentage had been appreciably larger, say more than 50 %, then man would suffer from oxygen poisoning (lung damage, reduced heart performance, changes in the retina of the eye, and reduced blood activity in the brain and the kidneys). And if the percentage of oxygen were too low, then body cells would suffer from a lack of oxygen. The brain is especially sensitive.

A greater percentage of oxygen would result in an easily inflammable earth – there would be frequent forest and open space fires, and metals would corrode and rust very quickly. On the other hand, if the percentage were as low as 10 %, it would not be possible to light a fire.

Nitrogen, which amounts to 78 % of the atmosphere, is the other main component, and all the other gases make up only 1 %. In contrast, the atmosphere of Venus consists for 96.4 % of carbon dioxide, and Mars's atmosphere contains 95 % of this gas. In large quantities carbon dioxide is a deadly poison for living organisms. Its concentration on earth is only 0.03 %, which is three hundredths of a percent. On the other hand, only traces of oxygen, so essential for life, are found in the atmospheres of Venus and Mars.

The available quantity of nitrogen is of crucial importance for living organisms. It ensures sufficient absorption of radiation, the correct dilution of oxygen, and the correct thickness of the atmosphere. If the envelope of air around the earth had been thicker, then too much sunlight would have been filtered out, and the process of photosynthesis in green plants would have been adversely affected. The importance of nitrogen becomes clear when other possible substitutes like ammonia, sulphur dioxide, hydrogen sulphide, carbon monoxide, or methane, are considered. All these gases are extremely poisonous and can destroy life. In addition, they are chemically unstable in the presence of oxygen and water.

7. The correct density of the atmosphere: The importance of this aspect should also not be underestimated. If the air were less dense, we would be subjected to fatally large doses of ultra-violet and X-rays, and fairly large meteorites would bombard us. The density of the atmosphere depends on the mass of the earth, and on the surface temperature. Because of its reduced gravity, a smaller earth would not have been able to retain the required amount of air and water. The mass and gravitational attraction of the earth are exactly correct for holding the required quantities of oxygen, nitrogen, and carbon dioxide. In addition, the air protects us from gamma rays and X-rays. The ambient temperatures are evened out, reducing extreme conditions, and the weather cycles can proceed accordingly.

8. The required quantity of ozone: Only a small part of the invisible ultra-violet rays of the sun (wave-length less than 0.36 μm) penetrates down to the surface, thanks to a very special property of the atmosphere. In the stratosphere, 10 to 50 km high, ozone is found in extremely small quantities – only one gas molecule out of one hundred thousand is a tri-atomic ozone molecule (O_3). This tenuous veil of ozone is however essential for life on earth, because it absorbs practically all the injurious ultra-violet rays having wave-lengths of between 0.29 and 0.32 μm.

9. The correct size of the moon: The tides are caused by the moon, and the inter-tidal zones are the habitat of a wide variety of organisms. If the moon were too small, tidal effects would be negligible, and if it were appreciably larger, the resulting high tides would be catastrophic.

10. The earth is fairly smooth: The earth is remarkably smooth, even when the highest mountains and the deepest ocean trenches are taken into consideration. If the earth could be reduced to a sphere having a diameter of one meter, the unevennesses would be only one millimetre above and below sea level. This means that fairly large areas are inhabitable.

11. The earth's magnetic field: The strength of the earth's magnetic field is approximately 0.35 Gauss on the surface. In contrast, Jupiter's field measures 4.2 Gauss, being the strongest magnetic field of all the planets. The magnetic field of the earth is very useful for navigation, but it also acts as a shield which deflects the injurious solar radiation known as the solar wind.

12. The earth – a watery planet: In conclusion we now discuss the most important feature of the earth which is absolutely essential for life, namely water. Without water, no life of any kind could exist. Water is not only found in the oceans, in lakes, and in rivers, but everywhere. In comparison to the wide plains of Mars, the stony deserts of the moon, and the craters of Mercury, the Sahara desert is a wet sponge. Water is found all over the earth, brought by clouds, now here, now there. Sometimes it rains and sometimes it snows, and even when the rains stay away in the deserts, nightly dews still bring moisture. In his book, *Wind, Sand, and Stars*, French author, *Antoine de Saint Exupery*, extolled and illustrated the importance of water for living organisms as follows:

> "Water! Water,
> you have no taste, no colour, and no aroma.
> You cannot be described.
> You are desired and liked even if you are
> unknowable …
> As an indescribable delicacy
> you refresh us through and through.
> All diminished powers are restored by you.
> Thanks to your blessing all the lost fountains of
> our souls are replenished.
> You are the most desirable thing on earth."

Covering 71 % of the surface, the **oceans** are unique to the earth. The fact that this amount of water is here in liquid form cannot be over-emphasised. Most of the matter of the universe consists of hot gases (as in the stars), or is deeply frozen (for example on the outer planets). The oceans act as an enormous reservoir of heat, their total volume being 1,370 million cubic km. For this reason they have an important moderating effect on the climate. Islands in the Gulf Stream enjoy a mild oceanic climate even at a latitude of 62°, while places in Siberia at this same latitude are subject to a severe continental climate – the average temperatures on the Faeroes Islands vary between 3.2 °C in January and 10.6 °C in July, while it changes from −43.5 °C to +19.0 °C in Yakutsk. If the earth had less water, then temperature changes would be considerably greater. In addition, the oceans are an important and essential source of food.

The total quantity of the water on earth amounts to 1,400 million cubic kilometres. This water is continually being cycled from and to the oceans, lakes, rivers, ice (in glaciers and at the poles), and ground water. The total quantity of water vapour in the atmosphere is about 13,000 cubic kilometres, which is less than one hundred-thousandth of the total quantity of water, but it is of crucial importance for the climate and thus also for living organisms. If all atmospheric water were spread evenly over the surface (510 million km^2), the earth would be covered to a depth of 25 mm. Considering that the average annual precipitation is 970 mm, it means that the water vapour in the atmosphere must as a whole be exchanged at least forty times per annum. At temperate and circumpolar latitudes the precipitation is much greater than the average, and this comprises an appreciable portion of the global heat transfer cycles. The major ocean currents like the Gulf Stream which transports warm water northwards, and the Humboldt Current (cold water), also carry large amounts of heat. In addition, the continuous evaporation of water from the oceans, aided by the trade and other winds blowing over thousands of kilometres, irrigates the continents which would otherwise be desiccated. The water cycle enables life to exist on earth, which would not have been possible without "the weather".

The present ratio between land and water areas on earth is not a random combination. (Before the Noahic flood other conditions prevailed [G3, p 103-120]). If the quantity of water on earth were 10 % greater, then the sea level would be 300 m higher, flooding most of the continental areas. On the other hand, if the amount of water were less, the land areas would be much greater and the climate much worse, so that large regions would be arid.

After being welcomed on board, airline passengers are usually given information about course, height, and outside temperature. At a height of 10,000 m the temperature of the air outside the cabin is a constant − 50 °C. You may not be aware of this fact, but the low temperature prevailing at heights of 5 to 20 km, is essential for life on earth. Water vapour freezes at these heights because of the low temperature, and the resulting ice crystals continue to grow until they become so heavy that they fall towards the surface. In this way water is prevented from escaping into space, so that the earth will be wet and not dry out for thousands of years.

Another very important property of water is that it reaches its greatest density at a temperature of 4 °C. At this temperature its density is 1.0 g per cubic cm, and it becomes less dense at higher as well as lower temperatures. At 0 °C the density of ice is 0.917 g per cubic cm. This is the reason why ice floats on water, which is the only substance that has these unusual properties. This means that aquatic organisms like fish can survive even the coldest winters in lakes, rivers, and dams. When a body of water freezes, the ice, being lighter, floats on the water, while the heavier water below does not become colder than 4 °C. If the ice were heavier, water in lakes, etc. would freeze from the bottom up and fish would be queezed to the surface where they would all die from asphyxiation.

With a value of 4.187 kJ/kg × K, water has nature's greatest **specific heat**[32]. This extremely high value (compared with lead 0.129; iron 0.452; gold 0.129; copper 0.382; alcohol 2.43; olive oil 1.97; quick silver 0.14) means that water is the best storer of heat of all substances. This is of great importance for the earth: The oceans thus form an enormous heat storer for the energy irradiated from the sun

---

32 **Specific heat** is the amount of heat needed to increase the temperature of a unit mass (e. g. 1 g or 1 kg) by 1 °C or 1K (= Kelvin). According to the old unit of heat and energy, the calorie (cal), water had the specific heat of 1.0 cal/gK. The calorie was defined as the amount of heat necessary to heat 1 g of water by 1 K – to be exact, from 14.5 to 15.5 °C. In the current SI system (International System of Units), the Joule (J) has replaced the cal. The conversion is 1 cal = 4.1868 J.

without a notable variation in temperature at different times of day. The oceans also form a considerable buffer for air temperature fluctuation. In addition, the oceans do not freeze in the winter. This is of fundamental importance for all types of marine life, as well as for the widely temperate climate formation which we have here on earth. A major transportation of heat takes place in the ocean current due to the high specific heat. With this tremendous amount of heat, the Gulf Stream (also called North Atlantic Stream in the North) keeps much of the North Atlantic free of ice in the winter. If the specific heat of water were considerably lower, then the earth would have a very different and much more unfavourable climate. It would be much colder in Europe, for example and the regional climate would be different and would change much quicker. Water's high specific heat is also of immense importance for living beings: an influx in the amount of heat has little effect on the temperature.

The extremely high **specific evaporation heat**[33] of water is also of great importance for the earth: On one hand, this hinders the ground from drying out, and on the other hand, as condensation heat, it forms the main source of heat in the higher geographical latitudes. The transporta-

---

33 **Specific vaporisation heat** (below boiling-point referred to as specific evaporation heat) is the amount of heat needed to convert 1 g of liquid into a gas without increasing the temperature. The vaporisation of a liquid takes place at its boiling point, that is for water at 100 °C. However, at a lower temperature, single molecules begin to escape from the liquid to the gas phase. This process is called evaporation. Heat is used in evaporation, too and thus an evaporated liquid cools down. The evaporation heat is dependant on the temperature (for water at 20 °C this is 2449 kJ/kg). As a rule, the evaporation heat decreases as the temperature increases. During the process of liquefaction of steam, the same amount of heat is emitted (specific condensation heat). Specific vaporisation heat of a number of substances (at boiling-point):

water	2256.3 kJ/kg
quick silver	283.9 kJ/kg
ethyl alcohol	844.9 kJ/kg
ethyl ether	360.1 kJ/kg

tion of condensation which comes from the sub-tropics to higher latitudes in atmospheric circulation thus also presents a great transportation of heat which is set free in the clouds in the process of condensation. This effect contributes considerably to the moderation of the temperature fluctuation between pole and equator. Living beings can use the high vaporisation heat to regulate their body temperature since much surplus heat can be emitted by the loss of a small amount of fluid.

Being finely tuned in various ways, the watery earth obviously provides hospitable conditions for all life forms.

Summary: We have only mentioned and discussed some of the many conditions that are required for life on earth – the most important and most conspicuous geophysical, mechanical, thermal, and other tangible aspects. Each and every one of the above-mentioned properties makes the earth unique. It is truly remarkable that all requirements are met on this one planet. All these conditions are mutually intertwined, making our planet ideally suitable for living organisms. Any unbiased observer would agree that all these features had been wisely planned and conceived.

We take life for granted, and only realise the earth's wonderful suitability when we compare it to other possible scenarios. The solar system contains striking counter examples of all the favourable conditions prevailing on earth. We find cosmic purgatories, frozen deserts, poisonous cauldrons, and cosmic voids. Conditions and substances on all the other planets and moons are absolutely hostile to life. It seems that the Creator is telling us something important through the currently increasing amount of planetary researches. This message is already found in Psalm 104:24: "How many are your works, O LORD! In wisdom You made them all; the earth is full of your creatures." God asked Job some questions to point out the fine balances between the parameters prevailing on the earth: "Where were you when I laid the earth's foundation? Tell me if you understand. Who marked off its dimensions? Surely you know! Who stretched a measuring line across it?" (Job 38:4-5). Evolutionists believe that life developed through a process of adaptation, but no adaptation is possible where the astronomical and geophysical parameters are concerned. These must have been exactly correct right from the beginning.

A1.2 The Moon and the Earth

The moon differs from other moons in the solar system in many respects:

1. The earth's moon is relatively large: Relative to all the other planets the earth's moon is the biggest. The earth's diameter is only four times that of the moon, and its mass is only 81 times as great. With the exception of Pluto (Pluto/Charon = 2,284 km/1,192 km = 1.92), this ratio is at least 1,000 to 1 for the other planets.

2. Distribution of rotational energy: Rotational inertia is an important property of rotating objects. It is noteworthy that the orbital inertia of the moon around the earth is greater than the earth's own axial moment of rotation. Again, with the exception of Pluto, this is exactly the opposite situation than is the case for all the other planet-moon systems, where the planet's axial moment of rotation is many times greater than the orbital moment of the moon.

3. The angle of the moon's orbit: The angle between the earth's equator and the ecliptic (the plane of the earth's orbit around the sun) is 23.5°. But the moon's orbit does not coincide with the equatorial plane. On the contrary, it makes an angle of approximately 5° with the ecliptic, while the orbits of most of the other moons are fairly close to the parent planet's equatorial plane. If this were the case for our moon, then the polar regions would receive very little moonlight.

4. Consequences of the moon's orbital period and the duration of its own axial rotation: The moon takes 29.531 days to complete one orbit around the earth (the → synodic period), and its period of rotation around its own axis (→ sidereal rotation) is exactly the same. The result is that we always see the same face of the moon. For an observer on the moon the earth would appear to stand still in the sky, moving only a few degrees from its position according to the librational movements of the moon. On the other hand, the earth can never be seen from any location on the far side of the moon.

5. Albedo or reflectivity: The meaning of the Latin word *albedo* is "white colour"; it is another term for the reflectivity of surfaces which do not emit light. The moon reflects 7 % of the incident sunlight; this is very low compared to the reflectivity of the earth (39 %) and Venus (76 %). If the moon's albedo were appreciably greater, then moonlight nights would be much brighter than at present, and the diurnal bright and dark cycle would have been disturbed.

One might think that the Creator could have achieved the same result by employing a smaller body with a greater albedo. Yes, but then the tides would have been much less pronounced, and → solar eclipses could never occur.

6. Moon and tides: The moon's mass is the chief determining factor for tidal variations (the sun plays a minor role). A smaller moon would not have been able to cause the present high and low tides with all their beneficial effects. If the moon's diameter were doubled (mass increase eight fold), then the earth would be ravaged by an eight-fold increase in tidal effects. It is obvious that the moon has been wisely created.

The phenomenon of spring tides and neap tides: The period between one high tide and the next ($T/2$) is 12 hours and 25 minutes. The centre of gravity of the earth-moon system is located approximately 4,800 km from the centre of the earth, which is well below the earth's surface. The earth-moon system rotates around this point, with the result that centrifugal forces as well as the gravitational attraction of both the sun and the moon affect the earth and the oceans. Tides caused by the moon are 2.5 times as strong as those caused by the sun, so that the water of the sea piles up on the side facing the moon. Centrifugal forces are responsible for an equal pile-up on the opposite side away from the moon, with low tides occurring at places halfway between. The two pile-ups retain their positions relative to the moon, so that the tides move round the earth as it rotates. At the same time $T/2$ the moon also moves relative to the earth, with the result that the period from one high tide to the next is approximately 12 hours and 25 minutes. This delay exists because of the moon orbiting around the earth (sidereal orbit in $T_M = 27$ d 7 h 43 min 15.5 s = 655.71986 hours), the moon, as seen from a fixed position on earth will not be at the same position at the identical time the next day (sidereal rotational period of the earth: $T_E = 23$ h 56 min 4 s = 23.93444 h), but only $t = T - 24$ h = 24.84 h − 24 h = 50.5 minutes later. In other words, until the moon has reached the same position relative to an observed earth meridian (longitude) $T = 24.84^{34}$ hours elapse. This time lapse also exists between the moon rise on consecutive days and is called retardation (lat. *retardatio* = delay, slowing down of a process). If the moon were to assume the function of the sun, given the same conditions of movement, the solar day on earth would last 24 h 50.5 min.

---

34 **Synodic orbit:** $T = T_E \times T_M / (T_M - T_E) = 24.84$ h = 24 h 50.5 min
$T/2$ = period between on high tide and the next =
(24 h 50.5 min)/2 ≈ 12 h 25 min

The relative positions of the sun, the earth and the moon change continuously, so that the heights of the tides also vary from day to day. During full moon and new moon, the earth, sun, moon and earth lie in a straight line so that the tidal effects of the moon and the sun enhance one another, causing extra high and low tides, called spring tides. But when sun, earth and moon form a right angle, the two effects nearly cancel out, resulting in neap tides when the difference in height between high and low water is at a minimum.

In addition to the effects which the relative positions of the sun and the moon have on the tides, there are several other factors which also influence the tides in various ways: friction between the water and the ocean floor, the deflecting effect of the earth's rotation, and the shape and topography of ocean basins, the sea floor, and especially of the coastline. The Baltic Sea is practically tideless, in the Mediterranean Sea the tides vary by at most a few decimetres, the difference between low and high tides amounts to 3 m on the north-western coast of Germany, and up to 12 m in the bays of Brittany and Normandy. But in the Bay of Fundy on the east coast of Canada record differences of an average of 14.14 m are found. This considerable difference is caused by geographical conditions: The bay penetrates inland for a distance of 80 km between Nova Scotia and New Brunswick on the continent, and its mouth is 48 km wide. No sizeable rivers flow into this bay so that tidal waves run into a veritable cul-de-sac. In the Elbe river (Germany) tides travel a distance of 130 km inland. In the St Lawrence river (Canada) this has an effect 700 km up-river, but in the Bay of Fundy a lot of water accumulates at the upper end when the tide is in.

Some beneficial effects of the tides:

- Beaches are cleaned and washed by the regular ebb and flow of the tides. It has been found that the water in the shallow and nearly enclosed Wadden Sea on the north-western coast of Germany, is completely replaced every three years. This cleaning out and regeneration is essential for the unique ecology of that region.

- Tidal basins and mud flats are home to many kinds of organisms unique to this environment occurring in great numbers and densities. Up to 40,000 mud crabs (*Corophium volutator*) have been counted per square metre, and many thousands young mussels (*Mytilus edulis*) can settle on such an area.

- Tidal currents clean waterways regularly and keep them open for traffic.

- Some waterways become navigable only at high tide, being too shallow at other times. Passenger boats can only visit the North Sea island Juist (Germany) only when the tide is in.

- Although tidal energy has not yet been utilised on a large scale, it could be an economical source of power. Note: The friction caused by the continually moving masses of tidal currents, especially in shallow seas, has a braking effect on the speed of rotation of the earth. This amounts to a lengthening of the day by 0.0016 seconds per century.

A1.3 Some Facts about the other Planets and their Moons

All the planets move in elliptical orbits with the sun at one focus of the ellipse, as was discovered and formulated by *Kepler*. The planes of these orbits as well as their eccentricities (any value between 0 and 1), and the sense of rotation could have been quite random, but in actual fact:

The planes of the orbits differ by less than 3°, except in the case of Mercury (7°) and Pluto (17°).

All the planets revolve in the same direction around the sun.

Most of the orbital ellipses are very nearly circular with eccentricities less than 0.1. Again, Mercury ($e = 0.21$) and Pluto ($e = 0.25$) are the exceptions.

The major half axes a of the planetary orbits (except for Neptune) can be expressed in terms of the *Titus-Bode* sequence, namely $a/(1 \text{ AU}) = 0.4 + 0.3 \times 2^n$, where $n = -\infty, 0,$

Figure 9: *Comparative sizes of the planets, and particulars of their rotations.*

(a) Sizes: *This scale drawing shows the large differences in size of the planets. The diameter of Jupiter (the largest planet), measured at its equator, is 11 times that of the earth, and 47.4 times that of the smallest planet (Pluto). When volumes are compared, the differences are much greater. Jupiter's volume is 1,318.7 times as large as the earth (the line beginning with V/V_e) and about 100,000 times as large as the smallest planet. In the second line from the bottom, m/me, we see that Jupiter is 5,780 times as massive as Mercury (317.93/0.055).*

(b) Comparison of rotations: *The central horizontal line represents the orbital planes of the various planets which have been reduced to one plane for the sake of simplicity. Actually, these planes all lie within an angle of less than 7°, except for Pluto, whose orbital plane makes an angle of 17.1° with the ecliptic (the plane of the earth's orbit). The dotted lines represent the rotational axis through the poles, and the circular arrows indicate the direction of rotation. Except in the case of Venus, the axial rotation of all the planets coincides with the direction of rotation in their orbits around the sun (see Rule 4 about the → Laws of rotation in the Solar System). The rotation of Venus is retrograde, in the opposite direction. The speed of rotation of each planet is given below each arrow. It is noteworthy that the most massive planet, Jupiter, rotates the fastest; its day lasts only 9 hours and 50 minutes. This is 593 times as fast as Venus's period of rotation, which is the slowest. The axial tilt of each planet is also given in the sketch – this is the angle between its axis and a line perpendicular to its orbital plane. This angle is equal to that between the equatorial plane of the planet and its orbital plane. Note the large tilts of the axes of Uranus and Pluto; this causes exceptional day and night phenomena.*

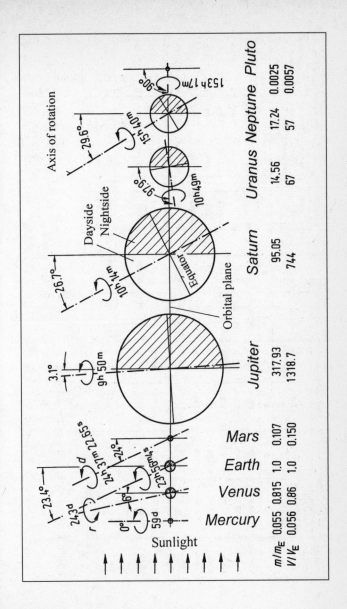

Planets and the sun	Orbits		Equatorial diameter		Mass m		Axial rotation			Orbital motion around the sun		
	Average distance from the sun in million km	Eccentricity e	in km	in Earth diameters	in kg	Earth = 1	Sidereal period in days	Direction of rotation	Axial tilt in degrees	Sidereal period in years	Direction of rotation	Angle with ecliptic
1	2	3	4	5	6	7	8	9	10	11	12	13
Mercury	57.9	0.2056	4,878	0.382	3.30×10^{23}	0.055	59	d	0	0.241	d	7.005
Venus	108.2	0.0068	12,104	0.949	4.87×10^{24}	0.815	243	r	6	0.615	d	3.395
Earth	149.5978	0.016722	12,756	1.000	5.976×10^{24}	1.000	0.99727	d	23.443	1.000	d	0
Mars	227.94	0.0934	6,764	0.530	6.42×10^{23}	0.107	1.02596	d	23.983	1.881	d	1.850
Jupiter	778.34	0.0485	142,200	11.148	1.90×10^{27}	317.93	0.40972	d	3.067	11.862	d	1.305
Saturn	1 427	0.0556	119,300	9.352	5.68×10^{26}	95.05	0.42639	d	26.733	29.458	d	2.490
Uranus	2 869.6	0.0473	52,000	4.077	8.70×10^{25}	14.56	0.45069	d	97.867	84.015	d	0.773
Neptune	4 496.7	0.0086	50,900	3.990	1.03×10^{26}	17.24	0.65277	d	29.567	164.788	d	1.773
Pluto	5 900	0.250	2,284	0.179	1.49×10^{22}	0.0025	6.3868	d	90	247.7	d	17.133
QB1	6 150	-								262		
Sun	-	-	1.392×10^{6}	109.1	1.989×10^{30}	333,000	24.25 at equator 35 near poles		7.25 Angle between equator and ecliptic		-	

Table 1: *Important data of the planets.*

| Moons | Orbits | | | Reciprocal mass (the planet taken as 1) | Angle α with planet's equator | Orbit around planet | |
	Average distance from planet in km	Eccentricity e	Diameter in km			Sidereal period in 24-hour days	Direction of rotation
1	2	3	4	5	6	7	8
Earth: 1 moon				1.0000			
Moon	384,404.4	0.0549	3475.6	81.3	5.14528	27.32166	d
Mars: 2 moons				1.0000			
Phobos	9,270	0.0210	20x23x28		1.1	0.3186	d
Deimos	23,400	0.0028	10x12x16		1.8	1.2624	d
Jupiter: > 16 moons				1.0000			
Amalthea (V)	128,000	0.003	270x165x150		0.4	0.498	d
Io (I)	421,600	0.0001	3,632	21,300	0.0	1.769	d
Europa (II)	670,900	0.0001	3,126	39,000	0.5	3.551	d
Ganymede (III)	1,070,000	0.0014	5,276	12,700	0.2	7.155	d
Callisto (IV)	1,883,000	0.0074	4,820	17,800	0.8	16.689	d
Himalia (VI)	11,470,000	0.1580	185		28	250.6	d
Elara (VII)	11,743,000	0.2072	75		28	259.7	d
Lysithea (X)	11,710,000	0.1074	36		29	259.2	d
Ananke (XII)	20,700,000	0.169	30		147	631	r
Carme (XI)	22,350,000	0.207	40		163	692	r
Pasiphae (VIII)	23,300,000	0.410	50		148	744	r
Sinope (IX)	23,700,000	0.275	36		157	758	r
Saturn: > 23 moons				1.0000			
Mimas	186,600	0.02	392	15,000,000	1.5	0.94242	d
Enceladus	238,000	0.0202	500	7,000,000	0.0	1.37022	d
Tethys	294,700	0.000	1,050	910,000	1.1	1.88780	d
Dione	377,500	0.0022	1,120	490,000	0.0	2.7369	d
Rhea	527,200	0.0010	1,530	250,000	0.3	4.5175	d
Titan	1,221,600	0.0289	5,140	4,150	0.3	15.945	d
Hyperion	1,483,000	0.1042	400x250x240	5,000,000	0.6	21.277	d
Iapetus	3,560,000	0.0283	1,440	300,000	14.7	79.330	d
Phoebe	12,950,000	0.1693	160		150	500.337	r
Uranus: 15 moons				1.0000			
Miranda	130,500	0.00	550	1,000,000	0.0	1.4136	d
Ariel	191,800	0.003	1,500	67,000	0.0	2.5204	d
Umbriel	267,200	0.004	1,000	170,000	0.0	4.1442	d
Titania	438,400	0.002	1,800	20,000	0.0	8.7059	d
Oberon	586,300	0.001	1,600	34,000	0.0	13.4633	d
Neptun: 8 moons				1.0000			
Triton	353,000	0.000	2,720	750	159.9	5.877	r
Nereid	5,560,000	0.749	500		27.2	359.881	d
Pluto: 1 moon				1.0000			
Charon	19,000		1,192			6.3868	

Table 2: *Some particulars of the moons in the Solar System.*

1, 2, …, 7, and 1 AU = 149,597,870 km, the distance from the earth to the sun, called an → astronomical unit.

Various salient properties of the planets as well as their sizes are illustrated in *Figure 9* and *Table 1*.

Except for Mercury and Venus, all the planets have one or more moons. Their numbers and some important particulars are given in *Table 2*. We will now discuss several interesting facts about the moons under 18 headings to emphasise the observed variations and the unexpectedness of many of them. It may sound repetitive, but it is necessary to point out that most of these phenomena do not fit in the evolutionary scheme of things.

Our knowledge of the Solar System has been greatly increased by the *Voyager 1* and 2 space probes. Many theories devised in the course of months or years had to be discarded shortly after reception of the first images. On the average, *Voyager 2* covered a distance of 1.7 million km per day. At this speed one could travel from London to Paris or from New York to Washington D.C. in about 17 seconds. On this "sight-seeing trip" from planet to planet the probes discovered many new things, like flashes of lightning on Jupiter, sulphurous eruptions on Io, one of Jupiter's moons, many thousands of rings around Saturn, Uranus's magnetic field and its corkscrew-like tail, and bizarre phenomena like ice eruptions on Triton, one of Neptune's moons.

1. Mercury: *Mercury* rotates once round its axis in 59 days, or, more precisely, the length of its sidereal day is 58.646 days. Its orbital period around the sun amounts to 88 days (the exact length of the sidereal year is 87.97 days). This means that the duration of one diurnal rotation is exactly equal to two-thirds of its year (58.646/87.97 = 0.666659 ≈ 2/3). This ratio has a very exceptional result: A → solar day on Mercury is exactly twice as long as a year (58.646/(87.97 − 58.646) = 2). A solar day is identical to the → synodical period of rotation round its axis and it lasts 176 earth days. Day temperatures of up to 450 °C have been measured, and at night this plummets to −170 °C. Because Mercury is close to the sun, the diameter of the sun as seen from the surface of Mercury is three times as big as it appears from the earth, and its area is nine times as large.

There is absolutely no trace of an atmosphere on Mercury, since all molecules which reach the → escape velocity[35] of 4 km/s, have disappeared long ago. The sky over Mercury is therefore always black even when the sun is shining, because there is no atmosphere to refract the rays of the sun. Any visitor to Mercury will however be blinded instantly in the extremely bright sunlight and the harsh glare being reflected from the surface.

2. Venus: *Venus* is the second planet out from the sun and the eccentricity of its orbit is only 0.0068, which means that it is very nearly a perfect circle. The two inner planets, Mercury and Venus, whose orbits are smaller than that of the earth, do not move farther than a certain angular distance from the sun as seen from earth. This sun-earth-planet angle is called their elongation. They can only be seen during a certain period before sunrise or after sunset, as morning or evening star respectively. Venus is the only planet with a retrograde axial rotation, with the result that the sun rises in the west and sets in the east.

---

35 **Escape velocity:** A certain minimum speed is required to be able to escape from the gravitational pull of any planet or moon. The value v of this speed depends on the mass and the radius r of each planet according to the formula $v = SQRT(2Gm/r)$, where G is the gravitational constant. Small bodies such as the moon, Mercury, and most of the other moons (except Titan and Triton) do not have a detectable atmosphere, because the escape velocity is so small that it is exceeded by the thermal velocity of gas molecules. The speed of gas molecules increases with temperature and is inversely proportional to their mass. Consequently, the lighter gases like hydrogen, helium and methane escape before the heavier nitrogen, oxygen and carbon dioxide.

The sidereal period of rotation of Venus around its own axis is 243 days, the longest of all the planets, and its year is 224.7 days long. Its speed of rotation is 593 times slower than that of Jupiter, the fastest planet.

Venus is the only planet whose period of rotation around its own axis is longer than its orbital period. It follows that the length of one solar or → synodic day from sunrise to sunset is $(224.7 \times 243)/(224.7 + 243) = 116.8$ days. This is the time span of sunlit day plus dark night; this period is also called solar day or synodic duration of rotation. At the equator a Venus day lasts 58.4 earth days from sunrise in the west to sunset in the east.

Apart from the sun and the moon, Venus is the brightest celestial object to be seen from the earth. When 30 % of Venus' surface faces earth, it reaches its maximum magnitude of −4.4. This happens at time of its closest approach, when it may even be seen in daytime with the bare eye. The reflectivity (albedo) of Venus is 76 %, nearly double that of the earth (39 %). Only Enceladus, one of the satellites of Saturn, has a greater albedo. On the surface of Venus the percolating sunlight has an orange-violet colour, and the ambient temperature is about 465 °C, which is hot enough to melt lead. Although Venus is not the nearest planet to the sun, it is, surprisingly, the hottest. It has a heavy, thick atmosphere consisting of carbon dioxide and nitrogen. Atmospheric pressure on the surface is 90 times as much as on earth, corresponding to the pressure at a depth of 900 m below the surface of the sea. Clouds of sulphuric acid float in this dense atmosphere – the same acid which is used in car batteries.

3. Mars: There is a gigantic 4,500 km long canyon on *Mars* which is up to eight km deep and 200 km wide. Compared to this, the Grand Canyon in Arizona (1.5 km deep and 28 km wide) is a tiny scratch. Like our moon, Mars also has many impact craters, which measure up to several hundreds of kilometres in diameter. The highest mountain in the Solar System is found on Mars: Olympus Mons is 20 km high and its base measures 500 km (the height of Mt Everest is "only" 8,842 m).

4. Phobos, one of the moons of Mars: Before *Phobos* and *Deimos* had been discovered by *A. Hall* in 1877, it was regarded as an unwritten law that the orbital period of a satellite had to be longer than the period of rotation of the parent planet. Phobos, the inner companion, is an exception to this rule, since it travels once around Mars in only 11 hours and 6 minutes (0.3186 days), compared to Mars's own period of rotation of 24 h 37 min (1.02596 days). It is therefore unique in the solar system as being the only moon which rises in the west and sets in the east, as seen from the surface of the parent planet. And this happens 2.2 times during the course of one Martian day, because of the numerical ratios involved, namely $(1.02596 - 0.3186)/0.3186 = 2.2$.

Both moons of Mars are extremely dark and peculiarly misshapen. Measuring $28 \times 23 \times 20$ km, Phobos resembles a potato more than a sphere. In 1959 a Soviet astrophysicist *J. Shklovsky* speculated about the possibility that it could be a hollow artificial satellite placed there by unknown intelligences. He believed in a strange and distant intelligence, rather than in the Creator of heaven and earth Who reveals Himself abundantly in the Bible.

5. Jupiter and its moons: Representing 60 per cent of the mass of all the planets and moons in the solar system, *Jupiter* is the largest and most massive planet. Surprisingly, its axial speed of rotation is the fastest (9 h 50.5 min at the equator and 9 h 55 min at higher latitudes). Jovian days are the shortest in the solar system, apart from some asteroids which also rotate quite fast. This fast speed of rotation causes Jupiter to be a flattened ellipsoid rather than a true sphere. Its coefficient of flattening[36] is 1:16, which is much more pronounced than that of the earth (1:298), so that its diameter through the poles is fully 8,800 km shorter than that measured at the equator. Jupiter is the brightest object in the night sky because of its size and the strong albedo of its atmosphere. Only Venus is brighter, but it cannot be seen at night. The "Great Red Spot" on Jupiter has been visible for 300 years – since the invention of telescopes. This spot is so large that the earth could fit inside it three times. Its exact nature was determined by the *Voyager 1* space probe in 1979: It is a gigantic hurricane in which raging winds of ammonia gas speed around at 200 km/h. At the perimeter speeds of up to 500 km/h have been measured.

The four largest moons of Jupiter, *Io, Europa, Ganymede*, and *Callisto*, were the first natural satellites to be discovered, apart from the moon. *Galileo Galilei* was the first person to observe them (1610) and they are appropriately referred to as the Galilean moons. The orbits of the five inner moons (see *Table 2*) are nearly circular, and they coincide with Jupiter's equatorial plane. But the outer moons revolve in strongly inclined and fairly eccentric orbits. The satellites numbered VI, VII, and X (*Himalia, Elara*, and *Lysithea*) form a group with approximately the same average distance (11.7 million km) and the same orbital inclination (28° to 29°). Moons VIII, IX, XI, and XII (*Pasiphae, Sinope, Carme*, and *Ananke* form a second group revolving in a retrograde direction, contrary to Jupiter's

---

36 **Rotational flattening:** Most of the planets resemble ellipsoids of rotation rather than true spheres, meaning that their diameter a at the equator is larger than the polar diameter b. The coefficient of flattening is defined as the ratio $A = (a-b)/a$, i. e. the difference between the equatorial and the polar diameters divided by the diameter at the equator. For the earth this amounts to 1:298.25 because $a - b = 42.77$ km and $a = 12,756.27$ km.

own direction of rotation at an average distance of more than 20 million km. These retrograde orbits cannot be explained in evolutionary terms. It should be noted that the names of retrograde moons have been chosen to end with an "e".

6. Io, one of the moons of Jupiter: *Io* is about 5 per cent larger than the moon, and its surface temperature is −146 °C. Except for earth, Io is the most exceptional object in the solar system because of its many unusual features. Only earth, Io, and Triton (one of the moons of Neptune) exhibit volcanic activity. Tremendous lava flows have been observed on Io. Measurements made on the images received from the Voyager space probes indicate that clouds of volcanic matter are ejected to heights of 100 km, and, in one case, even up to 300 km. Nine concurrently active volcanoes were identified. A certain fraction of the volcanic ash escapes into space, never to fall back. One of the prime factors driving volcanic eruptions on earth is steam, but there is no water on Io, and it is thought that the principal driving forces are gaseous sulphur dioxide and sulphur itself. The earth's volcanic activity is caused by the heat generated by radioactivity in the interior. But Io's mass is only one sixth of the mass of the earth and its heat reservoir is much smaller. If the solar system really were more than four thousand million years old as evolutionists believe, then all volcanic activity on Io should have ceased long ago. The biblical account of a young creation (not more than 10,000 years old) provides a more acceptable model. It has been found that a large electric current of five million amperes, caused by the fast passage of Io through Jupiter's strong magnetic field, flows continually between Jupiter and Io. Io's surface is relatively smooth, and it is quite colourful, exhibiting shades of red, yellow, orange, brown, blue, black, and white.

7. Ganymede: With its diameter of 5,276 km *Ganymede* is not only *the largest moon* of Jupiter but of the entire planetary system. It is even larger than Mercury and Pluto, but its density is only one-third that of Mercury. Ganymede's surface consists of two types: One part has many craters, and on the other there are relatively few craters, but many typical fissures. The fissures are between 300 and 400 m deep and they occur in parallel groups which form bands 100 to 200 km wide. Individual fissures are separated by distances of 3 to 10 km.

8. Saturn and its moons: With its diameter of approximately 120,000 km *Saturn* is the second largest planet of the solar system. At the equator its period of rotation is 10 h 14 min (near the poles it is 10 h 38 min) and its polar diameter is only 108,000 km, making it the planet with the largest coefficient of flattening (1:10). With its specific gravity of 0.7 g per cubic cm, it is the only planet that is less dense than water. As seen through earth-based telescopes, the smallest discernible detail on the surface of Saturn is the size of Africa. But the resolution was improved to between 5 and 10 km by *Voyager 1* in November 1980. The most prominent feature of Saturn is its system of rings. Thousands of individual rings, consisting of trillions of chunks of ice and rock, have been discovered. The diameters of these fragments range from a few millimetres up to several metres. The outer diameter of the ring system is about 300,000 km and it is surprisingly thin, only a few kilometres. One of the most interesting discoveries was the dark spokes radiating up to 105,000 km outwards across the bright B-ring. Other planets also have ring systems, namely Jupiter, Uranus and Neptune, but these are much less spectacular.

In regard to size and density, Saturn's moons differ appreciably from those of Jupiter. They are less dense, and their density increases with the distance from Saturn.

Whereas nine moons were known previously, their number has now been increased to more than twenty, thanks to the space probes. The smallest moons have diameters of only about 30 km, and all the minor satellites are bound in their rotation. This means that their period of rotation around their axes is exactly equal to their orbital period, so that the same face is always turned to the planet, like earth's moon. Two interesting satellites discovered by *Voyager 1*, known as S-10 and S-11, have approximately the same size (diameter = 700 km) and their orbits are very nearly identical. Their distance from Saturn is 149,000 km and they follow each other at a constant angular distance.

9. Saturn's moon Titan: With its diameter of 5,140 km *Titan* is nearly as big as Mars and is the second largest moon in the solar system. *Voyager 1* raced past Titan on 12 November 1980 at a distance of only 4,500 km and its speed was 60,000 km/h. *Mazursky*, one of the persons responsible for analysing the received images, determined that Titan had more ordinary rock than other moons, and that it had a nitrogen-rich atmosphere, like the earth. It is ironical that such an atmosphere has been found in the outer reaches of the solar system and not closer to home as might have been expected.

The space probe came closer to Titan than to any other body during its entire voyage and the resolution was excellent, but hardly anything on the surface of this cosmic "orange" could be recognised. It looked like a fluffy, seamless tennis ball and no contours or structures were found. The reason: It is covered by a dense, thick layer of fog. The mass of gases and vapours pressing down on one square kilometre of the surface is ten times as much as is the case on earth. But the atmospheric pressure is only 1.5 times that of the earth, because Titan's mass is only one 45th as large.

The earth and Titan are the only two planet-sized bodies in the solar system which have a nitrogen-rich atmosphere, 82 % nitrogen in the case of Titan. Titan is exceptional in being the only moon that has an atmosphere worth mentioning. Its temperature is − 180 °C, and at this temperature the six percent methane in the atmosphere plays a role similar to water on earth. At this low temperature methane can be a solid, a liquid or a gas, and we have the remarkable phenomenon on Titan that there are glaciers consisting of frozen methane, lakes filled with liquid methane, methane raindrops, and even methane snow.

10. Saturn's moons Dione and Tethys: Following in the same orbit as *Dione* itself, there is another moon, Dione B, located at an angular distance of 60°. Each of these two satellites lies on one vertex of an equilateral triangle with Saturn itself on the third corner. Moons which behave like this, are called "Trojans". A similar situation holds for *Tethys*: two small satellites occupy Trojan positions, one leading Tethys by 60°, and the other trailing 60° behind.

11. Saturn's moon Iapetus: *Iapetus* is unique. It has a bright side and a dark side; the dark hemisphere reflects only three to five percent of the incident sunlight, making it one of the darkest surfaces in the solar system. On the other hand, the remaining area reflects fully one half of the light falling on it.

12. Other moons of Saturn: A crater measuring 130 km in diameter was discovered on the greyish-white ice-covered surface of *Mimas*. This is remarkable, seeing that the diameter of Mimas itself is only 392 km. It is also remarkable that one hemisphere of *Enceladus* escaped from the cosmic bombardment which struck *Mimas*, *Dione*, and *Tethys*, for example. One hemisphere has many craters, but the other side is unblemished. There is no scar or crater, which means that the surface is "young". This is one of the many examples in the universe exhibiting a random mixture of "young" and "old" features. It is not only the "young" features which indicate a recent creation, but also the mixture of supposedly "old" and "young" features together. Enceladus is nearly a perfect mirror which reflects close to 100 % of the incident sunlight. If it were as close to the sun as our moon, it would be five times as bright.

13. Uranus and its moons: The orbits of the five moons known before the Voyager discoveries (see *Table 2*), are nearly circular. With the exception of Miranda, the angle between their orbital planes and Uranus's equatorial plane is less than one-tenth of a degree. The entire system is, however, very unusual: The angle between the equatorial plane and the ecliptic is 97.9°, which means that the axes of Uranus and of these moons nearly coincide with the orbital plane of the planet. This orientation is unique, and seasonal variations in the incidence of solar light differ completely from those of the other planets. A year on Uranus lasts approximately 84 earth years. At the moment its south pole points towards the sun, and its north pole is in perpetual darkness. After 42 years the situation will be reversed (see *Figure 10*). Ten further moons were discovered as a result of Voyager's visit to Uranus. Their diameters range from 50 to 170 km and they are surprisingly dark, having albedos of only 0.05. Since 1988 they were given the names *Puck, Portia, Juliet, Cressida, Rosalind, Belinda, Desdemona, Cordelia, Ophelia,* and *Bianca*.

14. Neptune: Like the other three large planets, *Neptune* is also a gas giant, consisting mainly of hydrogen and helium. Only the outer atmospheric layers containing methane, are visible, and this gives Neptune a blue colour, because methane absorbs the orange and red wavelengths and reflects blue light. As Jupiter has its red spot, so Neptune has a "dark spot" where hurricane-like

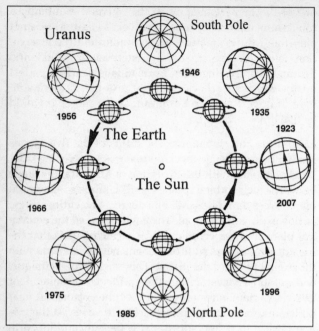

Figure 10: *Uranus as seen from the earth*
The axis of Uranus very nearly lies in its orbital plane, making an angle of about 98° with a line perpendicular this plane. This situation is unique in the solar system and it causes exceptional seasonal variations in the way solar energy is distributed. The changing view of Uranus as seen from the earth during one cycle of 84 years is shown [L2]. Every so often one pole points towards earth, then, 21 years later, equatorial regions can be seen, and after a further 21 years the other pole is turned towards the earth.

storms occur. This is remarkable, seeing that the prevailing temperature of the outer layers of the atmosphere is −220 °C. *James Pollack* of NASA remarked on this detail [K2, p 132]: We have reached the point at which we cannot even explain why the wind on Neptune blows so fiercely. Everywhere, from Venus to Neptune, we find extremely strong winds of 100 to 500 m/s. We have to consider that both the sun irradiation to each individual planet and the heat which each emits from its centre are completely different. The only outstanding exception is the earth. Here we measure average winds of 15 m/s.

15. The moons of Neptune: Up to the middle of 1989 two moons of Neptune were known: *Nereid* and *Triton*. In all, *Voyager 2* photographed six further minor moons (designated N1 to N6: *Proteus, Larissa, Galatea, Despina, Thalassa, Naiad*). They are shapeless clumps of ice, measuring from 50 to 420 km in diameter. Up to a distance of about 1,000 times the diameter of Neptune, there is no single moon except for Triton. Then Nereid is encountered far out. *Voyager 2* did not see so much moon-free space during all its other visits; this is quite exceptional. The eccentricity of Nereid's orbit is 0.749, which is the largest value for any moon. Its distance from Neptune varies between one million and ten million km. Having a diameter of 2,720 km Triton is the biggest moon of Neptune. Its axial period of rotation is 5.9 days which is the same as its orbital period. It therefore always turns the same face to Neptune, just like our moon. Triton revolves in a retrograde direction, contrary to that of the planet itself. It is the only major satellite which does this. The seasons on Triton last 41 earth years; each pole "basks" in sunlight for 82 years, followed by 82 years of darkness.

16. Pluto and Charon: This outermost planet of the solar system is also the smallest, having a diameter of only 2,284 ± 18 km. It is even smaller than our moon. Its orbit is an elongated ellipse with an eccentricity of 0.25. At its closest, it is 4,425 million km from the sun and its greatest distance is 7,375 million km. At its perihel (i. e. point closest to the sun) it is even closer to the sun than Neptune, i. e. the orbits of Pluto and Neptune cross. The angle of inclination of its orbit is 17.1 degrees, which is larger than for any other planet. For an observer on Pluto the sun would not appear as a disk, but it would resemble a bright star, appreciably brighter than our full moon.

The diameter of Pluto's moon, *Charon*, is 1,192 ± 34 km, and its orbital period is exactly equal to the period of rotation of Pluto around its axis, namely 6 days 9 hours and 17 minutes. This synchronous orbit is unique in the solar system. From the surface of Pluto, Charon always seems to "stand still" in the sky. Although Charon's orbit is circular, its plane is nearly perpendicular to the orbital plane of Pluto, which, in its turn, is nearly perpendicular to its equatorial plane. As in the case of Uranus, very unusual daily and seasonal rhythms prevail.

It is noteworthy that the planet closest to the sun (Mercury) as well as the most distant planet (Pluto) are the smallest planets. In addition, their orbits have the greatest inclinations (Mercury 7°, Pluto 17.1°) and the largest eccentricities (respectively 0.206 and 0.248). Another remarkable fact is that two of Pluto's years are exactly equal to three of Neptune, its nearest neighbour.

17. Magnetic fields of the planets: Like the earth, several other planets have magnetic fields, namely Mercury, Jupiter, Saturn, Uranus, and Neptune. Measuring 6.2 Gauss[37], Jupiter's magnetic field is the strongest. Its magnetic field is 14 times as strong as that of the earth, and it extends nearly 750,000 km into space on the side facing away from the sun. At the other extreme, the strength of Mercury's magnetic field is only one-hundredth that of the earth. And Uranus has a very unusual magnetic field: the magnetic axis makes an angle of nearly 60° with the axis of rotation. It is thus the most strongly inclined magnetic field in the solar system.

---

37 **Gauss:** Gauss is the unit of measurement of magnetic field strength; Tesla (T) is also used, and the conversion formulas are: $1 \, Gs = 10^{-4} \, T$, $1 \, T = 1 \, Vs/m^2$.

18. The size of the Solar System: From end to end the solar system measures 11,800 million km. This distance is, however, only 1/7000 of the distance to the nearest star, Alpha Centauri. The mass of the biggest planet, Jupiter, is only 1/1000 of the sun's mass, and even if all the planets and their moons were lumped together, their total mass would be only a fraction more than one-tenth of one percent of the sun's mass.

If you want to memorise the sequence of the planets, a mnemonic phrase like the following might help: "**M**y **V**alley on **E**arth **M**ay **J**ust **S**erve **U**s **N**ow **P**erhaps". This represents the first letters of the names Mercury, Venus, Earth, Mars, Jupiter, Saturn, Uranus, Neptune, and Pluto.

A tenth planet, provisionally called QB1, was discovered in 1992: On the night of 30th August 1992, *Daniel Jewitt* from the University of Hawaii and *Jane Luu* from the Berkley University of California experienced a sensation. With a 2.20 metre telescope on the peak of the volcano Mauna Kea, in Hawaii, they registered an extremely weak object in the constellation Pisces. It was confirmed that that this was a small planet, at present 41 astronomical units away from the sun and therefore beyond Pluto. This object received the provisional name 1992 QB1 [X1]. If we assume a circular orbit, then the distance from the sun would be in accordance with an orbiting time of 262 years. This small planet is 200 – 300 km and thus ten times smaller than Pluto and notably smaller than Ceres (1023 km in diameter). Ceres is the largest of the asteroids, i. e. the small planets between the Mars and Jupiter orbit. On 23rd March 1993, a further small planet with the magnitude 23, was discovered and given the provisional name 1993 FW [X2]. Further research will show whether these two objects are the only planets beyond Pluto or whether they belong to a further family of small planets.

The solar system (heliosphere) ends there where the solar wind meets the interstellar gas in the form of a shock wave. This transitional region, known as the heliopause, was detected by *Voyager 1* when an increase in the strength of radio waves in the range 2 to 3 kHz was observed. The heliopause extends from 40 AU from the sun to 100 AU.

A1.4 Surprising Facts about the Sun and the Moon

"And God made the two great lights, the greater light to rule the day, and the lesser light to rule the night" (Gen 1:16).

The apparent diameters of both the sun and the moon, as seen from the earth, vary periodically. Because of the differing nature of their orbits, they do so in quite a different pattern/cycle. Yet calculations show that their *average* apparent diameter is *identical*, to a high degree of precision. In fact, 27 times a year, they are exactly the same. At such times a neat, total eclipse is possible. This apparent design feature seems hard to dismiss as merely a sticking coincidence.

The creation account tells us of a greater and a lesser light, in other words, of the sun and the moon. The context makes it clear that the relative light intensities of the two heavenly bodies is meant, not their relative dimensions. In this chapter, however, we look closely at the significant and unexpected facts concerning their physical sizes. A remarkable phenomenon of our solar system has been the subject of accurate investigations made by the author.

The actual diameters of the sun, the earth, and the moon differ widely:

Sun: 1,392,700 km   [L2, Vol 2, p 243]
Earth: 12,756 km at equator   [L2, Vol 1, p 200]
Moon: 3,476 km   [L2, Vol 2, p 5]

The average centre-to-centre distances are:

Sun to earth: 1 AU = 149,597,870 km   [L2, Vol 1, p 199]
Earth to moon: 384,403 km   [L2, Vol 2, p 5]

The apparent size of an astronomical body depends on its distance from the observer. The following discussion mainly concerns the sun and the moon. Some preliminary remarks are now required to explain the calculations below.

Introductory remarks: When an object moves away from us, it seems to become smaller and smaller. The angle, α, which it subtends at the observer, is given by the formula $\tan \alpha = h/L$, where h is the actual size of the object, and L its distance. The angle α is measured in degrees. When dealing with very small angles, minutes and seconds (of arc) are used, where $1° = 60$ minutes $= 3,600$ seconds, also denoted as follows: $1° = 60' = 3,600''$.

In *Table 3* the subtended angles of an object measuring 1 metre (that is, $h = 1$ m) are shown. The distances vary from 1 m to 1,000 km, increasing by factors of 10:

Distance L	α in degrees	α in ''	α in ° ' ''
1 m	45.00000000 °	162,000.00''	45° 0' 0.00''
10 m	5.71059313 °	20,558.13''	5° 42' 38.13''
100 m	0.57293869 °	2,062.57''	34' 22.57''
1,000 m	0.05729576 °	206.26''	3' 26.26''
10,000 m	0.00572957 °	20.62''	20.62''
100,000 m	0.00057295 °	2.06''	2.06''
1,000,000 m	0.00005729 °	0.21''	0.21''

Table 3: *The angles subtended by an object measuring 1 m, at various distances.*

On the other hand, using the formula $L = 1/\tan \alpha$, the entries in *Table 4* give the distances an object of 1 m must be removed to subtend angles of $1°$, $1'$, and $1''$, respectively:

177

α	Distance of a 1 m object	Distance of a 16 mm coin
1°	57.3 m	92 cm
1′	3,437.7 m	5,500 cm
1″	206,264.8 m	330,000 cm

Table 4: *The distances at which a 1 m object and a 16 mm coin respectively subtend angles of 1°, 1′, and 1″.*

It can be seen from *Table 4* that one second of arc is an extremely small angle: the apparent size of a 1 m object at a distance of about 200 km, the distance between London and Cardiff in England or between Sydney and Taree in Australia (at this distance a 1 m object can of course no longer be seen by the bare eye). When the angle is one minute of arc, the distance is nearly 3.5 km. A 16 mm coin at a distance of 92 cm subtends an angle of 1°, and the angle is 1′ when it is 5,500 cm distant.

Sun, earth, and moon: We now consider the angle subtended by an astronomical body when it is viewed from another one. The average distances[38] are used in the subsequent calculations:

---

38 **Average distance of a satellite:** The average distance of a satellite from its parent body, when its orbit is elliptical, is defined as follows: Consider the mass M of the parent body and the mass m of the satellite, as point masses, and regard the orbit as a circle with radius r. If this imaginary system has the same sidereal period as the actual system, then r is taken as the average distance.

The sun as seen from the earth: α = 32.0056'
Earth as seen from the sun: α = 0.2945'
The moon as seen from the sun: α = 0.0807'

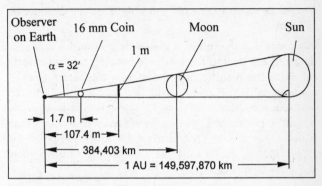

Figure 11: *Various objects subtending an angle of 32' at the observer's eye (distances not to scale).*

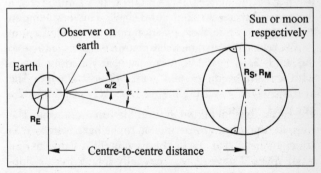

Figure 12: *Diagram required for calculating the apparent diameter.*

The given angle α is called the apparent diameter. The apparent size of the sun as seen from earth is equal to that of a 16 mm coin held at a distance of 1.7 m. But, conversely,

179

the earth can hardly be seen from the sun; it has the apparent size of a 16 mm coin at a distance of 190 m, a mere point of light. And the moon is even smaller, the size of a 16 mm coin at a distance of 680 m. An object measuring 1 m subtends an angle of 32 minutes of arc at a distance of 107.4 m.

We know that the orbits of the earth around the sun, and of the moon around the earth are not circular, but elliptical, with the result that the apparent diameters change continuously. The actual variations during the course of one year are shown in *Figure 13*. These results were computed by means of *Kepler's* second law, which states that equal areas are covered during the same periods (see *Figure 15*)[39] . *Figure 13* reveals a surprising result, which will now be discussed.

1. The sun as seen from the earth: The bold curve A indicates the apparent size of the sun as seen from the earth, during the course of a year. At its closest approach, called the **perihelion** (Greek *perí* = around, near, *helios* = sun), the sun subtends an angle of 32.549'. This happens on 2 January. At its farthest position on 5 July, called **aphelion** (Greek *apó* = distant, *helios* = sun), the angular size of the sun is 31.479'. Curve A is very nearly a cosine graph with an amplitude of $32.1'' = (32.549' - 31.479')/2$. The average value of A is $(32.549' + 31.479')/2 = 32.014' \approx 32'$.

The earth's orbital period around the sun is one year. The elapsed time from one perihelion to the next, is known as an anomalistic year, Y_a. Its duration is 365 d 6 h 13 m 53 s = 365.2596412 days. It is fractionally longer than a side-

---

39 **Data used:** The following data were used in the calculations (the variables *a* and *c* are defined in Fig. 15):
Earth-moon distance at apogee: $a + c = 406,740$ km
Earth-moon distance at perigee: $a - c = 356,410$ km
Earth-sun distance at aphelion: $a + c = 152,100,000$ km
Earth-sun distance at perihelion: $a - c = 147,100,000$ km

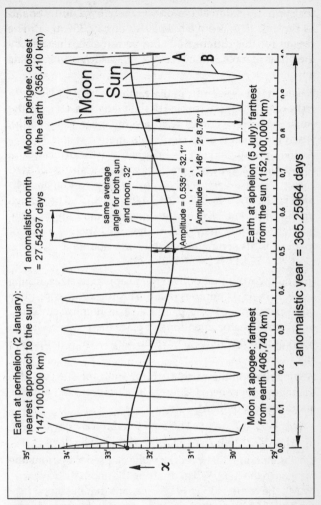

Figure 13: *The apparent diameters of the sun and the moon as seen from the earth. Curves A and B depict the changes during the course of one year.*

181

real year (→ sidereal period), namely by 4 minutes and 44 seconds ($Y_s = 365$ d 6 h 9 m 9 s = 365.256354 days). The reason for this difference is the perturbations caused by the other planets. But curve A is exact for an anomalistic year.

2. The moon as seen from the earth: Curve B in *Figure 13* represents the apparent size of the moon as seen from the earth. At **perigee** (Greek *perí* = around, near, *gaia* = earth), when the moon is at its closest, its angular size is 34.139'. At the opposite side of its orbit when it is furthest from the earth (the **apogee** point), its apparent size is 29.847'. Curve B is also very nearly a cosine graph and its amplitude is (34.139' − 29.847')/2 = 2.146' = 2' 8.76". The change in the apparent size of the moon is thus appreciably greater (4 times) than that of the sun. Another point of interest is its average angular size, found as follows: (34.139' + 29.847')/2 = 31.993' ≈ 32'.

It is noteworthy that both average apparent sizes are the same, namely 32 minutes of arc. This unexpected result is quite exceptional. Is this merely an astronomical curiosity, or did the Creator intentionally place these two bodies in the required positions to have the same average apparent size?

Analogously to the earth's orbit around the sun, we also distinguish between a sidereal lunar month, M_s, and the anomalistic month, M_a:

M_s = 27 d 7 h 43 m 11.5 s = 27.32166087 days
M_a = 27 d 13 h 18 m 33.2 s = 27.54297685 days.

One lunar anomalistic month is the elapsed time from one perigee to the next. When dividing the anomalistic year Y_a by M_a, the result is 13.2614. This means that the moon passes 13.2614 times through its perigee during one anomalistic earth year. Because this factor is not an integer, the relative positions of curves A and B change from year to year.

3. Further details: It also follows from *Figure 13* that curves A and B intersect 26 or 27 times during the course of a year. At these points the apparent sizes of the sun and the moon are equal, as observed from the earth, although it will only be seen to be such when the moon is full[40].

When curve B lies above A, the moon appears to be larger than the sun. A total eclipse of the sun is only possible when the apparent size of the moon is larger than that of the sun, but certain other conditions also have to be met (see Chapter A1.5).

A1.5 Solar Eclipses

Eclipses of the sun occur when the dark new moon moves in such a way between the sun and the earth that its shadow falls on the earth.

In the event of a total eclipse the sun is completely blotted out when the moon's umbral (total) shadow moves across the earth's surface.

A solar eclipse can only occur when all three of the following conditions are fulfilled, and no other moon can meet these requirements:

1. The average apparent sizes of the sun and the moon must be equal, as has been established in the previous chapter (A1.4). The actual diameter of the moon is only one-four hundredth that of the sun, but it is 400 times nearer, so that both have the same apparent size. This ratio is so surprisingly exact, that it is logical to conclude that it was intentionally devised by the Creator, rather than merely being a coincidence. Since the orbits of both the earth and the moon are elliptical, the apparent sizes of

---

40 **Point of observation:** The relevant calculations are mathematically exact only when the observer is situated on the line joining the centres of the earth and the sun, or the line from the centre of the earth to the centre of the moon.

the sun and the moon vary continuously (as has been discussed in Chapter A1.4). Three types of solar eclipses can be distinguished, depending on the relative apparent sizes at that time.

A *total eclipse*, when the sun seems to disappear completely behind the moon, can only occur when the apparent size of the moon is larger than that of the sun. If the moon appears to be smaller than the sun, then the eclipse will be annular (*ring-shaped*) even when the moon passes directly between the earth and the sun. A third possibility is that the moon does not pass directly between the sun and the observer; then we have a *partial eclipse*.

2. If the moon's orbit coincided exactly with the ecliptic (the plane of the earth's orbit), then solar eclipses would have occurred once a month, at new moon. But the moon's orbit is inclined at an angle of 5° 9' to the ecliptic, so that it is above or below the plane of the earth's orbit most of the time. Then its shadow cone cannot strike the earth. The second requirement is thus that the moon must be at or near the so-called nodal line[41] of its orbit. Solar eclipses can only occur when the angle between the nodal line and the sun or the moon is less than 18° 31'. (A total eclipses of the moon is only possible when this angle is less than 12° 15'.)

3. Solar eclipses can only occur when the sun, the earth, and the moon lie very nearly in a straight line, because the apparent sizes of the sun and the moon are approximately equal.

---

41 **Nodal line:** The line of intersection of the orbital plane of the moon with the ecliptic is known as the moon's nodal line. The spatial orientation of this line changes continuously as it rotates in the ecliptic with a period of 18.6 years. The angle between the equatorial plane of the earth and the ecliptic is a constant 23.5°, and the nodal line of the moon rotates in the ecliptic, with the result that the angle between the plane of the moon's orbit and the earth's equatorial plane varies between 18.5° and 28.5° (23.5° ±5°).

Let $n =$ the sum of the number of solar eclipses plus the number of lunar eclipses in a single year, then we find that the maximum value of n is 7. This was the case in 1935 and in 1982. In 1935 there were 5 solar and 2 lunar eclipses, and in 1982 there were 4 and 3 respectively. The minimum annual value of n is 2, and both will be solar eclipses, as was the case in 1984 for example. Eclipses always occur in two's or three's. A lunar eclipse always precedes or follows a solar eclipse. The duration of a solar eclipse depends on the exactness of the concurrence of the above three conditions. Theoretically the longest duration of a solar eclipse is 7 minutes and 31 seconds, but the longest observed one lasted 7 min 8 s, which was quite exceptional. It occurred in the Philippines on 20 June 1955. Most solar eclipses last only a couple of minutes, and the shortest duration could be a fraction of a second. A total eclipse which was visible in the northern Atlantic Ocean on 3 October 1986, lasted only one-tenth of a second.

In the most favourable case when the moon is at its closest approach (perigee), its shadow on the surface of the earth has a maximal diameter of 264 km. This shadow rushes along the surface at an average speed of 580 m/s because of the rotation of the earth and the relative motions of earth and moon. In a 3000 km wide zone straddling the centre line the moon will partially cover the sun's disk, resulting in a partial eclipse. The centre line describes a certain curve on the earth's surface, which is determined by the apparent motions of the sun and the moon and the rotation of the earth about its inclined axis (see *Figure 14*).

A total solar eclipse can thus only be observed in a small region of the earth's surface. The zone of half shadow (penumbra) is much larger, so that partial eclipses are visible in fairly large areas. In contrast, lunar eclipses can be seen as long as the moon is above the horizon. Noting that a total eclipse of the moon can last up to 100 minutes, it can be observed over more than one hemisphere. At any given place on earth, lunar eclipses can be seen more frequently than solar eclipses, although 2 to 3 solar and only 1 to 2 lunar eclipses occur annually. In London for example, no solar eclipses were visible during the entire period from 875 to 1715. The exact ratio of the number of solar eclipses to lunar eclipses is 61:39, or approximately 3:2.

No exact or absolute dates are available for the early post-diluvial history of mankind. Certain events were timed in relation to others, but their times are also uncertain. The earliest date which could be determined exactly, was the battle between Medes and Lydians in the year 585 BC. This battle was interrupted when a solar eclipse scared both armies. The date was found to be 28 May 585 BC by means of exact astronomical calculations.

Figure 14: *Diagrammatic representation of solar eclipses (not to scale). Three types of eclipses can be distinguished according to the relative distances:*

1. Annular eclipse: The apparent diameter of the moon is less than that of the sun. The moon's umbral shadow does not reach the earth. Eclipse conditions (2) and (3) are met, but the moon is close to its apogee (the most distant point from the earth). Only the central part of the sun's disk is eclipsed, so that the outer ring is still visible.

2. Very brief period of totality: The apparent sizes of sun and moon are the same.

3. Total eclipse: The moon's apparent diameter is greater than that of the sun.

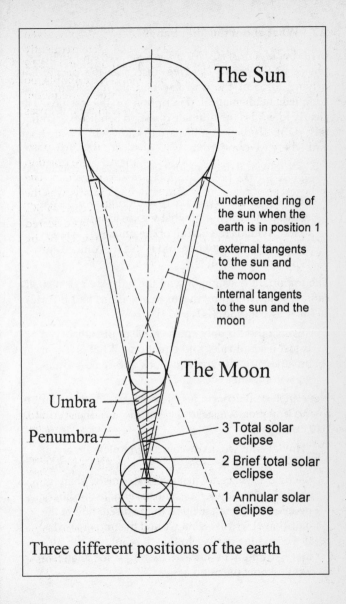

The Sun

undarkened ring of
the sun when the
earth is in position 1

external tangents
to the sun and
the moon

internal tangents
to the sun and the
moon

The Moon

Umbra

Penumbra

3 Total solar
eclipse

2 Brief total solar
eclipse

1 Annular solar
eclipse

Three different positions of the earth

A2. What about the "big bang"?

In his book, *A Brief History of Time*, the well-known British physicist, *Stephen W. Hawking*, discusses the primordial driving force of the universe and the possibility of a complete mathematical description of the cosmos. He clearly identifies the ultimate question behind everything [H1, p 13]: "Today we still yearn to know why we are here and where we came from."

His astrophysical deliberations lead him to the conclusion in his last chapter that [H1, p 171]:

> "We find ourselves in a bewildering world. We want to make sense of what we see around us and to ask: What is the nature of the universe? What is our place in it and where did it and we come from? Why is it the way it is?"

The important question of why the universe exists at all, cannot be answered by means of equations and theories, as *Hawking* concedes [H1, p 174]:

> "Even if there is only one possible unified theory, it is just a set of rules and equations. What is it that breathes fire into the equations and makes a universe for them to describe?"

Nevertheless, he concludes his book by limiting himself to the equations, instead of looking for their Author [H1, p 175]:

> "However, if we do discover a complete theory, it should in time be understandable in broad principle by everyone, not just a few scientists. Then we shall all, philosophers, scientists, and just ordinary people, be able to take part in the discussion of the question of why it is that we and the universe exist. If we find the answer to that, it would be the ultimate triumph of human reason – for then we would know the mind of God."

Like so many other astronomers and physicists, *Hawking* tries to explain the universe without acknowledging its Creator. But *Isaac Newton* (1643 – 1727), one of the greatest physicists of all times, and a predecessor of *Hawking* in the same chair at Cambridge University, firmly believed that the solar system had been created by God. The idea that the solar system emerged from a chaotically rotating, diffuse, undifferentiated glob of matter began with *Kant* (1724 – 1804). Influenced by the doctrine of evolution, many present-day cosmologists describe the cosmos in terms of evolutionary development, and most of them accept the so-called big bang theory. According to this theory, the universe (the totality of all space and matter) originated about 10 to 20 thousand million years ago as an inconceivably small volume of space which has been expanding ever since. The most important observation supporting this idea, is the "red-shift" of the light of distant stars; this red-shift purportedly indicates that the universe is expanding. The expansion itself cannot be observed directly, but it is inferred, because light coming from distant galaxies seems to have longer wave-lengths with increasing distance. This phenomenon is ascribed to the Doppler effect, namely that the wave-lengths of light are "stretched out" when galaxies move away from one another. This would be the case when the entire universe is expanding. The inferred expansion is extrapolated so far into the past, that it is thought that the cosmos was originally compressed into an inconceivably hot and dense "cosmic egg". The general background radiation detected by means of balloon and satellite observations, is regarded as strong evidence for this theory.

Space does not permit a full discussion of all the scientific counter arguments, but it should be emphasised that many discoveries made in recent years with improved instruments and improved observational methods have repeatedly shaken the big bang theory [F1]. Interpretations of the available facts in terms of the currently held cosmological models very quickly lead to unresolvable inconsistencies, and there is an increasing number of astronomers who raise substantial arguments against the big bang theory.

Instead of containing a homogeneous distribution of mass, the universe is in fact extremely heterogeneous. Matter is concentrated in zones and planes around relatively empty regions. Two astronomers, *Geller* and *Huchra*, embarked on an ambitious and tedious measuring programme with the expectation of finding additional support for the big bang model. By compiling large star maps, they hoped to demonstrate that matter is uniformly distributed throughout the cosmos, as was required by the big bang model. The result was a big surprise: The more progress they made with a cartographic overview of a region of space, the clearer it became that distant galaxies are clustered like cosmic continents beyond nearly empty reaches of space. The big bang model was strongly shaken by this discovery.

It should be added that the visible galaxies do not contain enough mass to explain the existence and distribution of these structures. But the big bang model was not discarded. Instead, the existence of "dark matter" was postulated. Without any shred of evidence for its existence, the mass of this dark matter was supposed to be ten times as much as the visibly observed mass.

We now quote a number of criticisms of the big bang theory:

Ernst Peter Fischer, a physicist and biologist of Constance, Germany, introduced the sensational article of *Halton C. Arp*, an American astronomer, as follows [F3, p 112]:

"If the popularity of a model is regarded as a measure of its correctness, then we should not be worried about the big bang idea that the universe originated in a primordial explosion. This theory is not only accepted by physicists, but it has become so widespread amongst laymen that doubts about it are regarded with amazement. Although big bang cosmologists still do not know what happened during the very first fractions of the first second after the postulated primordial event, this gap seems to be becoming vanishingly small. The big bang is a source of amusement, and sells well, even in magazines which otherwise have little to do with science. The warning given by *Carl Friedrich von Weizsäcker*, is lightly ignored, namely that a society which accepts the idea that the origin of the cosmos could be explained in terms of an explosion, reveals more about the society itself than about the universe. Nevertheless, the many observations made during the past 25 years or so, which contradict the standard model, are simply ignored. When fact and theory contradict each other, one of them has to yield."

Arp, born in 1927, was attached to the world-famous Mount Wilson Observatory near Pasadena, USA, and to the Las Campanas Observatories in California. At present he is a visiting scientist at the Max Planck Institute for Astrophysics in München-Garching. He explains the reasons for rejecting the big bang model in a notable article, "Der kontinuierliche Kosmos" (The continuous cosmos) [F3, p 112-173].

"Since antiquity ideas of the universe varied widely, depending on assumptions about factual observations. The current idea of a big bang has been the standard model for about 60 years. But, in the mean time, the number of observations that negate the assumption that the red shift of the light of distant galaxies can be explained by recessive motions, is increasing" [F3, p 113][42].

"… in my opinion the observations speak a different language; they call for a different view of the universe. I believe that the big bang should be replaced, because it is no more a valid theory" [F3, p 118].

Professor *Hans Jörg Fahr* of the Institute for Astrophysics at Bonn University, Germany, writes in his book, *Der Urknall kommt zu Fall* (The demise of the big bang) [F1, p 9-10]:

"The universe originated about 20 thousand million years ago in a cosmic explosion (the big bang), it has been expanding ever since, and it will continue to do so until the end of time … This sounds convincing, and it is accepted by all present-day mainstream 'natural philosophers'. But it should be obvious that a doctrine which is acclaimed noisily, is not necessarily close to the truth. In the field of cosmology the widely supported big bang

───────────────

42 **We mention only a few of *Arp*'s arguments:**
1. There are many "young" galaxies in our neigbourhood, but the big bang theory requires that all galaxies should be old.
2. The observed background radiation is a measure of the temperature. This weak radiation is regarded as the present-day remnant or echo of the original explosion. Since it is assumed that all galaxies originated at the same time, it should be possible to determine their small-scale effects on the temperature of the background radiation. The measured amount of radiation is, however, extremely constant. The more accurate the measurements become, the more constant are the results. The observed deviations are less than one-ten thousandth or one-hundred thousandth. Such variations have been heralded as the most positive proof of the big bang, but an increasing number of astronomers regard them as negative proof.
3. The age of the universe and the age of the oldest stars do not agree. Supporters of the big bang theory try to solve this problem by making the geometry of the universe more complex, or by postulating the existence of a repellent force in addition to the attracting force of gravity.

theory is not more convincing than other alternatives. In fact, there are surprisingly many alternatives."

In his voluminous work *Fahr* discusses many scientific details which contradict the big bang theory.

Dr *James Trefil*, professor of physics at Mason University, Virginia, accepts the big bang model, but he concedes that a state of emergency exists regarding fundamental aspects of explaining the universe [T1, p 9 & 68]:

"There is no real reason for the existence of galaxies in the far reaches of space, but there they are, and the observed variety of their shapes and sizes is confusing ... One of the most intractable problems of cosmology is to explain their existence in terms of the big bang model. They should actually not be there, but they are. It is difficult to describe the frustration that this simple fact causes among scientists."

My own opinion is that as long as we try to explain the universe apart from the Creator and without regard to biblical affirmations given by Him, we will be swamped by ingenious ideas, none of which would be close to the truth.

A3. Detailed Explanations of some Astronomical Concepts

We now discuss and explain a small selection of astronomical concepts which may help to clarify some questions that the reader may have after reading this book. In alphabetical sequence the topics are:

- Astronomical unit
- Celestial sphere (firmament)
- Constellation
- Elliptical orbit
- Inclination of the orbital plane of a moon
- Local group
- Pulsar
- Rotational features of the solar system
- Sidereal period
- Solar constant
- Solar day
- Star magnitude
- Synodic period

Astronomical Unit: The mean distance between the centre of the earth and the centre of the sun is called one astronomical unit (AU). It is often used to measure great distances in space. The exact definition is [G2, p 17]: The distance of one astronomical unit is equal to the semi major axis of the unperturbed circular orbit of an object with negligible mass which revolves around the sun at a sidereal angular speed of 0.017202098950 radians per day.

1 AU is given as 149,597,870 km in the list of astronomical constants (1976) of the International Astronomical Union (IAU). The orbital period of this imaginary object, calculated by means of the formula $2\pi/0.017202098950$, is 365 days 6 hours 9 minutes and 56.015 seconds, which is exactly the length of the earth's sidereal year.

Celestial sphere: If one ignores the distance of a star and only considers the direction from which its light reaches us, all celestial bodies may be regarded as projections on a large sphere (with radius = 1) around us. One-half of this sphere (one hemisphere) is visible from any given position on the earth's surface at a particular moment.

One complete revolution comprises 360°, and one degree of arc is a one-dimensional unit of measurement. In the same way we may define a square degree as a unit of area on a sphere with radius 1 unit:

$$1 \text{ square degree} = (1°)^2 = (2\pi/360°)^2 = 3.046174 \times 10^{-4}$$

The area of a sphere is given by the formula $A = 4\pi r^2$. If $r = 1$, then the area of a unit sphere is: $A = 4\pi$, and this is equal to $4\pi/(2\pi/360°)^2 = (360°)^2/\pi = 41,253$ square degrees.

Example: The average apparent diameter of the full moon is $d = 32' = 0.5333°$ (see Chapter A1.4). In terms of square degrees its area is $A = d^2\pi/4 = (0.5333°)^2 \times \pi/4 = 0.2234$, meaning that the disk of the full moon can fit 184,660 times in the entire celestial sphere ($= 41,253/0.2234$).

Remarkable: When we turn our eyes to the night sky, we get the impression that only a small fraction of the surface of the heavens is covered with stars. However, if we include all the stars with a magnitude of 27, we arrive at a staggering conclusion: According to modern studies of star systems up to magnitude 27, the heavens has a star coverage of 70 – 80 per cent (*Science* V. 234 (1986), p. 1202)).

Constellation: During earliest times man grouped the stars and named conspicuous constellations. It is noteworthy that names of constellations are mentioned in one of the oldest books of the Bible, namely Job (Job 9:8-9, 38:31-32). We read in Isaiah 40:26 and Psalm 147:4 that God named all the stars. Did He pass some of these names on to man? The shape of the constellations results from their projection on the celestial sphere. When observed from another position in space, the constellations would look different.

Some northern constellations (the Big Bear, the Dragon, the Eagle, and the Swan) and some constellations of the zodiac (Gemini, the Scorpion, Libra) are easy to recognise from their names. But for most of the constellations a vivid imagination must have played a role in the name-giving. The names of many present-day constellations were derived from mythology: Legendary Greek figures (e. g. Pegasus, Perseus, Andromeda, Casseiopia, Berenice's Hair) are included, and even groups of constellations depict myths (e. g. Orion the hunter, accompanied by the large dog and the small dog, chases the bull, which confronts him with lowered horns).

When the southern hemisphere came under the attention of European astronomers during recent centuries, they also grouped and named those new constellations. Seafarers, requiring these stars for navigation, gave them arbitrary names based on their own maritime experiences (e. g. Sextant, Octant, Telescope, Ship's Compass, Seal, Poop Deck, Keel, Table Mountain, Swordfish, Bird of Paradise, Flying Fish, and Indian). Only a few of the southern constellations rightfully carry their names, like the Southern Cross.

The apparent course of the sun (the ecliptic) passes through 13 constellations[43] . Many of these bear the names of animals (e. g. Ram, Bull, and Crab). The so-called signs of the zodiac (Greek: *zodiakós kyklos* = animal circle) are the constellations lying on the ecliptic as seen from the earth.

---

43 The apparent annual path of the sun passes through several constellations. Normally we talk about 12 constellations but that is not correct (see chapter 8.3.1). In 1930, the *International Astronomical Union* accepted a total of 88 constellations with defined borders. If we presume this to be correct, then the apparent annual path of the sun actually passes through 13 constellations, not 12. Between Scorpio and Sagittarius we find Ophiuchus. Although the major part of this constellation is to be found north of the ecliptic, the apparent path of the sun still clearly passes through it.

Another property of the zodiac is that all the planets appear and move within the ecliptic. Because the earth revolves around the sun, the sun is seen in a slightly different direction each day. It appears that the sun moves along the ecliptic around the earth during the course of a year. This apparent orbit passes through the constellations of the zodiac. For example, on the first of January the sun seems to be in Sagittarius, the Archer. This constellation cannot then be seen at night, since it is overhead during the day, and thus invisible because of the brightness of the sun. In contrast, Gemini and its surroundings are clearly visible in January because the sun is on the opposite side. The position is reversed in July: The sun is located in Gemini which cannot then be seen. It should be clear that various constellations can be seen during the course of a year. Each zodiac constellation is visible at night for approximately six months at a time. These constellations are being misused by astrology to construct horoscopes (see Chapter 8.3.1).

The individual stars of a constellation are denoted by Greek letters together with the genitive of the Latin name, as was proposed by *Johannes Bayer* (1564 – 1617). Vega, the brightest star in Lyra, is designated Alpha Lyrae. In addition, some of the brightest stars have their own distinctive names (examples: Acrux = Alpha Crucis, Agena = Beta Centauri, Aldebaran = Alpha Tauri, Arcturus = Alpha Bootes, Betelgeuse = Alpha Orionis, Rigel = Beta Orionis, Sirius = Alpha Canis Majoris). A total of 88 constellations have been named. *Remark:* All the component stars are members of our own Milky Way.

Elliptical orbit: According to *Kepler's* first law the planets move in elliptical orbits around the sun, with the sun located at one of the foci (*Figure 15*). A similar situation holds for the moons orbiting a planet. The shape of an ellipse is characterised by its eccentricity, e, which is a dimensionless number. If we take c as the distance from a focus to the centre M of the ellipse, the value of e is given by the formula $e = c/a$, where a is half the length of the major axis. For a circle the foci coincide with the centre ($c = 0$), and its eccentricity is zero. Ellipses have eccentricities in the range $0 < e < 1$. When $e = 1$ the curve becomes a parabola, and when e > 1, we have a hyperbola.

If the major axis of an ellipse is twice as long as its minor axis ($b = a/2$), its eccentricity is 0.866, from the formula $c = \mathrm{SQRT}(a^2 - b^2)$. We have:

$$e = c/a = \mathrm{SQRT}\{1 - (b/a)^2\} = \mathrm{SQRT}\{1 - (1/2)^2\} = \mathrm{SQRT}(3/4)$$
$$= 0.866.$$

Aphelion (Greek *aph'helion* = away from the sun) is that point on the orbit of a planet where it is furthest away from the sun, and *perihelion* (Greek *peri* = around, near) is the point of closest approach. The corresponding terms for the orbit of the moon are *apogee* and *perigee* (Greek *gaia* = earth), where perigee refers to the nearest approach of an object orbiting the earth.

Example: The eccentricity of the orbit of Neptune's moon Nereid is $e = 0.749$, and the ratio of the semi-axes is $b/a = \mathrm{SQRT}(1 - e^2) = 0.6626$.

According to *Kepler's* second law, the line drawn from a planet to the sun, sweeps equal areas during the same time interval. This means that, if $t_1 = t_2$ in *Figure 15*, then $A_1 = A_2$. Consequently, the orbital speed of a planet is greatest at perihelion, and at aphelion it is at its minimum.

Inclination of the orbital plane of a moon: This inclination is the angle between the orbital plane of a moon and the equatorial plane of the mother planet. The rotation of the planet itself is from west to east, and the moons generally revolve in the same direction (see Rule 4 of the → rotational laws of the solar system). If this rule were universally applicable, then a given angle α of between $-90°$

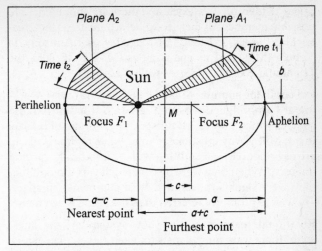

Figure 15: *Characteristics of an elliptical orbit*

and $+90°$ would uniquely describe the relevant relationships. But, in actual fact, there are cases where the sense of rotation is opposite or retrograde. This can be expressed mathematically with angles larger than $90°$. The angle between Neptune's equatorial plane and the orbital plane of its moon Triton is only $21.1°$, but, even so, Triton revolves in a retrograde sense with respect to the general rotation rule. If α is replaced by $180° - 21.1° = 158.9°$, then the rule is generally valid in mathematical terms. All angles in *Table 2* which are greater than $90°$ (or equal to $90°$), therefore indicate retrograde orbits where the moon rotates in a sense contrary to that of the mother planet. The sense of rotation of Jupiter's moons Ananke, Carme, Pasiphae and Sinope, as well as Saturn's Phoebe, and Triton (one of Neptune's satellites), is retrograde, indicated by "*r*".

Local Group: The cluster of galaxies which includes our Milky Way galaxy, is known as the Local Group. It comprises 17 identified galaxies, and there are about ten more possible members of this group, which includes the greater and the lesser Clouds of Magellan, the Andromeda Nebula (M31) and its companions (M32, NGC 305), the Triangular Nebula (M33), as well as Maffei 1.

Pulsar: In the summer of 1967 *J. Bell* and *A. Hewish*, working at Cambridge, discovered certain astronomical radio sources which they called pulsars. The number of pulsars in our Milky Way is estimated to be half a million. Pulsars are radio sources transmitting with a periodically varying intensity. When they were discovered, it was thought that they were signals transmitted by living beings in space. They were promptly referred to as the "little green men".

Rotational features of the solar system: At the latest count there were nine planets (or even eleven planets; see chapter A1.3, point 18) and 66 natural satellites (moons) in the solar system. Analysis of their motions reveals the following regularities or laws:

1. *Shape of the orbits of the planets:* All planetary orbits around the sun are ellipses which are close to circular. The only exception is Pluto, whose eccentricity is 0.250.

2. *Orbital planes of the planets:* All these orbits lie in approximately the same plane, the ecliptic. But with an angle of 17.13°, Pluto's orbit is quite exceptional.

3. Without exception *all the planets revolve in the same direction* around the sun.

4. *Axial rotation of the planets:* With the exception of Venus, all the planets rotate in the same direction about their axes as their orbital motion. There is no evolutionary explanation for the retrograde rotation of Venus.

5. *Inclination of axis:* The angle between the equatorial plane of a planet and the plane of its orbit is less than 30° (exceptions: Uranus, Pluto).

6. *Moons' orbits:* The orbits of most of the moons are nearly circular (see *Table 2* for exceptions; e g Neptune's Nereid and moons VI to IX of Jupiter).

7. *Planes of the moons' orbits:* The planes of the orbits of most of the moons coincide approximately with the equatorial plane of the mother planet, and they are nearly coplanar with the ecliptic. See Table 2 for exceptions; e. g. Jupiter moons VI to IX, Iapetus and Phoebe (Saturn), and the moons of Neptune.

8. Most of the *moons revolve in the same direction around the mother planet,* as that of the orbital motion of the planet around the sun (see *Table 2* for the exceptions, indicated by *r*).

The motion is designated as direct (letter *d* in *Tables 1* and 2), if it agrees with the rules (i. e. from west to east). If they rotate in the opposite direction, as is the case for Venus and some of the moons, it is regarded as retrograde (Latin *retro* = backwards, *gradus* = pace) (letter *r* in *Tables 1* and 2).

Sidereal period: (Latin *sidus, sideris* = stars): The sidereal period is the time required for one complete rotation (about its own axis), or one complete revolution (around the parent body). The word sidereal indicates that this period does not depend subjectively on a specific point of observation, but as it is seen from a distant star. At such a large distance the rays of light emanating from the local orbital motions of a planet or a moon are parallel, so that the actual movement of a complete revolution can be observed. Three cases can be distinguished:

1. *Planets:* The sidereal period of a planet is known as its sidereal year. It is the time required for one complete orbital revolution around the sun, i. e. the time interval between two successive transits of the same fixed star. The earth takes 365.26536042 days to complete one orbit along the ecliptic; this is the length of its sidereal year.

2. *Moons:* Similarly the sidereal period of a moon is the duration of one orbit around its mother planet.

3. *Axial rotation:* The sidereal period of rotation of a celestial body (the sun, the planets, and their moons) is the time required for it to rotate through an angle of 360° about its own axis. Or, in other words: The sidereal period is the time taken by the starry sky to complete one apparent revolution around the planet (or whatever body we are considering). The length of one sidereal day of the earth is 23 hours 56 minutes and 4 seconds = 86,164 s = 23.93444 hours.

Solar constant: The average amount of energy incident on the earth on a unit area during one time unit, is known as the solar constant. Its value is calculated above the atmosphere (AM0 = air mass 0) to exclude atmospheric effects, taking the earth to be a disk as seen from the sun. The projected area of the earth's surface is calculated as πr^2, and the solar constant E_o is s1.35 kW/m² ±3.4 %, the deviations being the result of the changing distance from the sun during the course of a year. The amount of energy which actually reaches the surface of the earth, varies greatly, depending on:

- the differences between night and day
- seasonal differences (periodical changes in the angle of incidence of the sun's rays through the atmosphere)
- changes in atmospheric conditions (e. g. clouds, fog, precipitation, dust) which also differ from place to place
- the different angles of incidence over one hemisphere (the geographical longitude and latitude of a given place)

The solar constant E_o has also been defined for other planets. At a distance of 0.723 AU the constant for Venus is 2.621 ±0.004 kW/m², and for Mars (1.52 AU) it is 0.593 ±0.001 kW/m².

When all the effects are averaged out (day and night, weather conditions, and geographical location), the global annual insolation (incident solar energy) E_m is 0.2345 kW/m² for the entire surface of the earth ($4\pi r^2$). The total daily insolation for different latitudes in the northern hemisphere is illustrated in *Figure 16* in 10° steps.

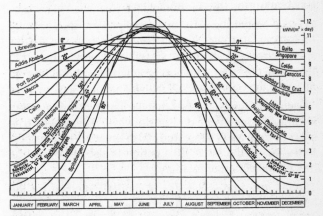

Figure 16: *Annual insolation above the atmosphere.*
The curves depict the seasonal changes in the amount of incident radiation at different latitudes, in steps of 10° from the equator (0°) to Spitsbergen (80°). The actual insolation at a given place on earth is appreciably less than the solar constant which is 1.35 kW/m² = 24 × 1.35 kWh/m² per day = 32.4 kWh/m² per day. In equatorial regions the amount of incident radiation is fairly constant during the course of a year.

Solar day: The time from one noon to the next, when the sun is again exactly overhead at a given longitude, is known as one solar day (in astronomical terms: the period from one meridian transition to the next). A solar day is slightly longer than the earth's period of rotation about its axis (=1 stellar day = sidereal period of rotation = 23 h 56 m 4 s = 86,164 seconds), because the earth moves approximately 1° of arc further along its orbit during the course of a day.

The apparent course of the sun through the sky is not uniform, because there are two superimposed deviations:

1. The earth's orbit is elliptical (and not circular). According to *Kepler's* second law its orbital speed is thus not constant during the course of a year.

2. Equal orbital segments on the ecliptic produce unequal projections on the equator. Thus, although the earth's speed of rotation about its axis (which is perpendicular to the plane of the equator) is constant, corresponding segments of the ecliptic are not equal.

The effect of these factors is that the length of the solar day is different for every day of the year. After every true solar day the earth's longitudinal orientation with respect to the sun is the same. This period is also known as the → synodic period of rotation.

The length of one solar day is similarly defined for the other planets. Mercury has the longest solar day, lasting 175.9 earth days, while Jupiter's solar day is only 9.8 hours long because of its high speed of rotation.

The average length of a solar day may easily be calculated for any planet if its sidereal period of rotation and its sidereal orbital period is known (see formula 1, → synodic period). Some examples follow, based on the data in *Table 1:*

Mercury: $T = (58.646 \times 87.97)/(87.97 - 58.646)$
$= 2 \times$ (Mercury's sidereal year) $= 175.9$ days

Venus: $T = (224.7 \times 243)/(224.7 + 243) = 116.8$ days

(The reason for the $+$ sign in the denominator is that Venus rotates in a retrograde direction.)

Mars: $T = (1.02596 \times 1.881 \times 365)/(1.881 \times 365 - 1.02596)$
$= 1.0275$ days $= 24.66$ hours

A solar day on Mars is only 40 minutes longer than on earth.

Star magnitude: The brightness of a star as it appears to us, is called its apparent brightness. Stars are arranged on a magnitude scale according to their brightness, denoted by m (Latin *magnitudo* = size). This scale of comparison has nothing to do with actual sizes. It was introduced by *Hipparchus* (190 – 125 B C) who classified the stars in six groups, 1m, 2m, …, 6m, where 1m indicates the brightest stars, and stars of the sixth magnitude are barely visible with the naked eye.

With the advent of the telescope it was necessary to extend this scale. The faintest stars which become visible when long exposure photographs are taken by the most sensitive instruments, have a magnitude of 23m. Their apparent brightness is the same as that of a burning candle at a distance of 28,000 km, which is more than ten times the distance from Paris to Moscow. The magnitude scale also has to be extended above 1m for many stars and planets, as well as for the sun and the moon: 0m, -1m, -2m, etc.

For computational purposes the brightness or magnitude of a star follows the fundamental psycho-physical law of *Fechner* and *Weber* (1859). According to this law, sense-impressions are proportional to the logarithm of the stimulus. If I is the intensity (stimulus) and m the magnitude (sense-impression), then the difference in magnitude, $m_1 - m_2$, between two stars, denoted by I_1 and I_2, is defined by the formula $I_1 / I_2 = 10^{(-0.4 (m1 - m2))}$.

Now $I_1 / I_2 = 10^{(-0.4 \times (m1 - m2))} = 10^{0.4 (m2 - m1)} = 2.512^{(m2 - m1)}$

so that the intensities (brightnesses) I_1 and I_2 of two consecutive magnitudes (i. e. $m_2 - m_1$) are in the ratio 1:2.512. If the magnitudes differ by 5, then the brightness ratio is $1:(10^{0.4})^5 = 1:10^2 = 1:100$. If the magnitudes differ by 10, this ratio becomes 1:10,000, and for a difference of 20 it amounts to 1:100,000,000.

All-in-all, the magnitudes of astronomical bodies vary from -26.86m (the sun) to 23m (the faintest optically observable star), a range of 50 classes of magnitude. The ratio of their apparent brightnesses is $1:10^{(0.4 \times 50)} = 1:10^{20}$, a number which cannot be envisaged. Exact magnitudes are expressed by using decimal fractions unlike practice in antiquity. The human eye can detect differences of 0.1 in apparent brightness. A capital M is used to indicate absolute brightness.

Synodic period: At a given moment a celestial body occupies a certain position relative to the sun. The time lapse until it is in the same relative position again, is known as its synodic period.

1. *Planets:* The synodic period of a planet T_{syn} is the time it takes to move once round and return to the same position relative to the sun as seen from the earth. The earth's orbital period is denoted by T_E, and that of the observed planet by T_P The three bodies, sun, planet and earth, have the same spatial orientation relative to one another after one synodic period of the planet. The same holds for any observer on any planet when looking at another planet.

$\omega_E = 360°/T_E$ Earth (sidereal period $T_E = 365.25$ days)
$\omega_P = 360°/T_P$ observed planet (sidereal period T_P)
$\omega_{syn} = 360°/T_{syn}$ The relative motion of the two bodies
$\qquad\qquad\qquad (T_{syn} = \text{synodic period})$
$\omega = $ Angular velocity

The following general equation can be used to calculate the synodic period T_{syn} of any planet or moon:

$$1/T_{syn} = 1/T_E - 1/T_P \qquad (1)$$
or: $\quad T_{syn} = T_E \times T_P /(T_P - T_E)$

In this equation T_E is the sidereal period of the planet on which the observer is located. This is usually the earth, but it could be any planet. T_p is the sidereal period of the observed planet or moon. T_{syn} is calculated in relation to this.

As seen from earth, only the synodic periods of the other planets can be measured. It can then be used to calculate their sidereal periods T_p according to formula (1).

Examples:

1. *One planet as observed from another:* As seen from earth, Mars's synodic period is given by $(365.25 \times 687)/(687 - 365.25) = 779.9$ days.

When Mars is observed from Jupiter, its synodic period is $(11.862 \times 1.8809)/(11.862 - 1.8809) = 2.235$ years $= 816.3$ days.

2. *Orbital period of a moon:* This is the duration from one phase of the moon until it is in that phase again, as seen from the mother planet. The synodic period of the moon is 29 days 12 hours 44 minutes and 2.9 seconds; this is the time from one new moon to the next, for example.

3. *Axial rotation of the planets:* The synodic period of rotation of a planet is identical to its true → solar day. It is the time required for a given meridian (longitude) to occupy the same position with respect to the sun again after one rotation.

Abbreviatons Used for the Books of the Bible

Books of the Old Testament (OT)

Gen	Genesis	Eccl	Ecclesiastes
Ex	Exodus	Song	Song of Solomon
Lev	Leviticus	Is	Isaiah
Num	Numbers	Jer	Jeremiah
Deut	Deutoronomy	Lam	Lamentations
Jos	Joshua	Ez	Ezekiel
Judge	Judges	Dan	Daniel
Ruth	Ruth	Hos	Hosea
1 Sam	1 Samuel	Joel	Joel
2 Sam	2 Samuel	Amos	Amos
1 King	1 Kings	Ob	Obadiah
2 King	2 Kings	Jona	Jonah
1 Chron	1 Chronicles	Mi	Micah
2 Chron	2 Chronicles	Nah	Nahum
Ez	Ezra	Hab	Habakuk
Neh	Nehemiah	Zeph	Zephaniah
Esther	Esther	Hag	Haggai
Job	Job	Zech	Zechariah
Ps	Psalms	Mal	Malachi
Prov	Proverbs		

Books of the New Testament (NT)

Matt	Matthew	1 Tim	1 Timothy
Mark	Mark	2 Tim	2 Timothy
Luke	Luke	Titus	Titus
John	John	Phlmn	Philemon
Acts	Acts	1 Pet	1 Peter
Rom	Romans	2 Pet	2 Peter
1 Cor	1 Corinthians	1 John	1 John
2 Cor	2 Corinthians	2 John	2 John
Gal	Galatians	3 John	3 John
Eph	Ephesians	Hebr	Hebrews
Phil	Philippians	James	James
Col	Colossians	Jude	Jude
1 Thess	1 Thessalonians	Rev	Revelation
2 Thess	2 Thessalonians		

References

[A1] Ahnert, P.: Astronomisch-chronologische
Tafeln für Sonne, Mond und
Planeten
VEB Johann Ambrosius Barth
Leipzig, 6th Edition 1988, 76 p.

[A2] Asimov, I.: Die Erforschung der Erde und des
Himmels
Deutscher Taschenbuch Verlag
dtv, München, 1987, 394 p.

[B1] Block, J. L.: Our Universe: Accident or
Design?
Starwatch, Wits 2050,
South Africa, 1992, 40 p.

[C1] Conradie, F.: Stargazing
Kransberg Communications,
Westonaria, 2nd Edition, 1991,
67 p.

[F1] Fahr, H.-J.: Der Urknall kommt zu Fall
– Kosmologie im Umbruch –
Franckh-Kosmos Verlag,
Stuttgart, 1992, 327 p.

[F2] Ferrari Der Stern von Bethlehem
d'Occhieppo, K.: Franckh-Kosmos Verlag,
Stuttgart, 1991, 148 p.

[F3] Fischer, Neue Horizonte 92/93
E. P. (Hrsg.): – Ein Forum der
Naturwissenschaften –
Piper-Verlag München, 1993,
238 p.

[G1] GEO Special   Weltraum
                        Nr. 8, 3. Quartal 1983

[G2] German, S.:   Handbuch der SI-Einheiten
     Draht, P.:   Vieweg-Verlag, Braunschweig/
                        Wiesbaden, 1979, 460 p.

[G3] Gitt, W.:   Das biblische Zeugnis der
                        Schöpfung
                        Hänssler-Verlag, 6th Edition 1995,
                        188 p.

[G4] Gitt, W.:   In 6 Tagen vom Chaos zum
                        Menschen
                        – Logos oder Chaos –
                        Hänssler-Verlag, Neuhausen-
                        Stuttgart, 5th Edition 1998, 238 p.

[G5] Gitt, W.:   Questions I have always wanted
                        to ask
                        CLV-Verlag, PO Box 11 01 35,
                        33661 Bielefeld (Germany),
                        2nd Edition 1998, 188 p.

[G6] Gitt, W.:   Did God Use Evolution?
                        CLV-Verlag, PO Box 11 01 35,
                        33661 Bielefeld (Germany),
                        1st Edition 1993, 159 p.

[G7] Gitt, W.:   What About the Other Religions?
                        CLV-Verlag, PO Box 11 01 35,
                        33661 Bielefeld (Germany),
                        1st Edition 1995, 159 p.

[G8] Gitt, W.:   If Animals Could Talk
                        CLV-Verlag, PO Box 11 01 35,
                        33661 Bielefeld (Germany),
                        2nd Edition 1998, 127 p.

[G9] Gitt, W.: Surprising Facts about the Sun and Moon
Creation ex nihilo –
Technical Journal, Vol. 9, no. 2, 1995, p. 259-262

[G10] Gitt, W.: In the Beginning was Information
CLV-Verlag, PO Box 11 01 35, 33661 Bielefeld (Germany), 2nd Edition 2000, 256 p.

[H1] Hawkins, S. W.: A Brief History of Time
– From the Big Bang to Black Holes –
Bantam Books, New York, 1988

[H2] Heckmann, O.: Sterne, Kosmos, Weltmodelle
Deutscher Taschenbuch Verlag dtv, München, 1980, 356 p.

[H3] Herrmann, J.: Großes Lexikon der Astronomie
Mosaik Verlag München, 2nd Edition, 1982, 407 p.

[H4] Herrmann, J.: dtv-Atlas zur Astronomie
Deutscher Taschenbuch Verlag dtv, München, 10th Edition 1990, 287 p.

[H5] Herrmann, J.: Das Weltall in Zahlen
Tabellenbuch für Sternfreunde –
Kosmos, Franckh'sche Verlagshandlung, Stuttgart, 1986, 127 p.

[H6] Hoffmann, K.-F.: Siehe, da kamen die Weisen vom Morgenland
– Geschichte oder Legende? –
Manuskript zum Vortrag vom 18.12.74 im Zeiss-Planetarium Berlin, Wilhelm-Foerster Sternwarte, 21 p.

213

[H7] Holbe, R.:   Zeitgeist
Knaur, 1991, 285 p.

[H8] Holzmüller, W.:   Unsere Umwelt – ihre Entwick-
lung und Erhaltung
B. G. Teubner Verlagsgesellschaft,
Leipzig, 4th Edition 1987, 135 p.

[K1] Keller, W.:   Und die Bibel hat doch recht
Econ-Verlag, Düsseldorf, 1959,
444 p.

[K2] Klingholz, R.:   Marathon im All
Ullstein-Verlag, 1992, 168 p.

[K3] Kroll, G.:   Auf den Spuren Jesu
Verl. Kath. Bibelwerk Stuttgart,
10th Edition 1988, 470 p.

[L1] Lattimer, D.:   "All we did was to fly to the
Moon"
Vol. I in the History-Alive Series:
A Mini-History of America's
Manned Moon Program
The Whispering Eagle Press,
Florida, 1985, 144 p.

[L2] Lexikon   Lexikon der Astronomie
Herder-Verlag, Freiburg, Basel,
Wien
Band 1: A bis Mizram, 1989, 432 p.
Band 2: Missing mass-Problem bis
ZZ Ceti-Sterne, 1990, 460 p.

[L3] Lovell, B.:   Das unendliche Weltall
– Geschichte der Kosmologie von
der Antike bis zur Gegenwart –
Deutscher Taschenbuch Verlag
dtv, München, 1983, 231 p.

[M1] Monod, J.:   Zufall und Notwendigkeit
Deutscher Taschenbuch Verlag
dtv, München, 3rd Edition 1977,
172 p.

[M2] Moore, P.:   The Guinness Book of Astronomy
– Facts & Feats –
Guinness Superlatives Limited,
2 Cecil Court, London Road,
Enfield, Middlesex,
2nd Edition 1983, 289 p.

[M3] Moore, P.,   Atlas des Sonnensystems
     Hunt, G.:   Herder-Verlag, Freiburg, Basel,
Wien 1985, 462 p.

[P1] Pagels, H. R.:   Cosmic Code. Quantenphysik als
Sprache der Natur
Ullstein, Berlin 1983

[P2] Pailer, N.:   Neues aus der Planetenforschung
– Unerwartete Ergebnisse durch
Weltraumsonden –
Hänssler-Verlag, 1993, 29 p.

[R1] Ross, H.:   Genesis One:
A Scientific Perspective
Wisemen Productions, Sierre
Madre, California,
Revised Edition 1983, 23 p.

[S1] Steidl, P. M.:   The Earth, The Stars, And
The Bible
Presbyterian and Reformed
Publishing Company,
Phillipsburg, New Jersey, 1979,
250 p.

[S2] Strobel, A.: Der Stern von Bethlehem
– Ein Licht in unserer Zeit? –
Flacius-Verlag, Fürth/Bayern,
1985, 79 p.

[T1] Trefil, J.: Fünf Gründe, warum es die Welt
nicht geben kann
– Die Astrophysik der Dunklen
Materie –
Rowohlt Taschenbuch-Verlag,
Reinbek, 1992, 249 p.

(The Dark Side of the Universe
Charles Scribner's Sons/
Macmillan Publishing Company,
New York, 1988)

[W1] Weigert A., Astronomie und Astrophysik
Wendler, H. J.: VCH Verlagsgesellschaft mbH,
Weinheim,
2nd Edition 1989, 329 p.

[W2] Weinberg, S.: Die ersten drei Minuten
– Der Ursprung des Universums –
München, 1980, 201 p.

(The First Three Minutes
– A Modern View of the Origin of
the Universe –
Basic Books, Inc., Publishers,
New York, 1977)

[W3] Weinberg, S.: Der Traum von der Einheit des
Universums
C. Bertelsmann Verlag, München,
1993, 320 p.

(Dreams of a Final Theory,
Pantheon Books, New York, 1993)

[W4] Weisbrod,   Dampflokomotiven deutscher
     Müller, Petznick: Eisenbahnen, Band 1,
     Alba-Verlag, Düsseldorf, 1976

[W5] Wright, R.:   Science, God And Man
     Time, January 4, 1993, pp. 46-50

[W6] Wuketits, F. M.: Evolutionäre Erkenntnistheorie
     als neue Synthese
     in: Herrenalber Texte Nr. HT 52,
     1983, pp. 29-41

[X1] Hahn, H. M.:   Gibt es den Planeten X? (Is there a
     Planet X?)
     Bild der Wissenschaft, 1/1993,
     pp. 92-93

[X2]–   Ein weiterer Kleinplanet jenseits
     der Plutobahn

     (A Further Small Planet Beyond
     Pluto's Orbit),
     Sterne und Weltraum 8-9/1993,
     p. 588

Werner Gitt

Did God Use Evolution?

160 pages
DM 4,80
ISBN 3-89397-725-X

Many well-known scientists are turning away from the synthetic theory of evolution in favour of a doctrine of theistic evolution. The reason for this trend is obvious, because no natural process has ever been observed where information originated spontaneously in matter.

It was hoped to close this gap by reverting to theistic evolution. According to this view God started the process of evolution and guided and steered it over millions of years. This idea has gained some popularity amongst Christians.

As an information scientist Werner Gitt critically analyses and rejects the assumptions and consequences of the doctrine of theistic evolution. His conclusions are fresh and startling.

Pocket-book

Werner Gitt

Questions
I have always wanted to ask

Pocket-book

160 pages
DM 3,80
ISBN 3-89397-184-X

Everyone who starts to take interest in
the Christian faith is confronted by
numerous questions. For each person
searching for God, there is a remarkable
tendency to ask the same questions.

There was therefore a need to collect
these questions and to answer them
in a short but adequate form. All the
questions which have been dealt with in
this book have one thing in common –
they are genuine questions. It is not
a book of cross-section answers for
Christian insiders, but tries instead to
take each problem seriously, which
occupies the minds of those who are
doubting, questioning and searching.

It is not at all a collection of hair-
splitting theological or constructed
theoretical points, but instead it handles
basic questions which have been the
result of a series of lectures given by the
author of this book. Unusual questions
have also been dealt with.

Werner Gitt

What About the Other Religions?

160 pages
DM 3,80
ISBN 3-89397-765-X

This book deals with a topic which often leads to heated discussions:

– There are so many religions. Are they all wrong, is there only a single correct one, or do all ultimately lead to the same goal?

– People with other religions are honest in their beliefs. They perform their prayers and sacrifices sincerely and trust fully in their religion. Surely God must also see it that way. If God is a God of love, must He not recognise all efforts to reach Him?

– Our times are characterised by understanding and tolerance. Shouldn't that also be the case between religions, as Frederick the Great (1712 – 1786) already believed: "Everyone should be saved in his own manner?" Isn't the Gospel highly intolerant, if it throws out all other ways and claims to be uniquely correct?

These are among the questions most often asked during discussions about faith. We need real answers to help us. The author provides a thorough, Biblically-based work, which allows one to orient himself in this field of conflict.

Pocket-book

Werner Gitt · K.-H. Vanheiden

If Animals Could Talk

128 pages
DM 3,80
ISBN 3-89397-760-X

Animals have very efficient communication systems, which they use to converse with one another. Nevertheless, they cannot speak to us in human language. The authors have taken it upon themselves to act as their verbal representatives. The animals take up several possible questions and deal with them in this imaginary conversation. The authors have, in this way kept the content narrative, lively and entertaining – without forfeiting scientific credibility.

This book has something for everyone, both young and not so young, experts and laymen alike.

Pocket-book